1967

MUSIC IN AMERICA

MUSIC IN AMERICA

An Anthology FROM THE LANDING OF THE PILGRIMS TO THE CLOSE OF THE CIVIL WAR, *1620—1865*

Compiled and Edited, with Historical and Analytical Notes,
by W. THOMAS MARROCCO, Professor of Music, University of California
at Los Angeles, AND HAROLD GLEASON, Consultant in Music,
Rollins College, Winter Park, Florida

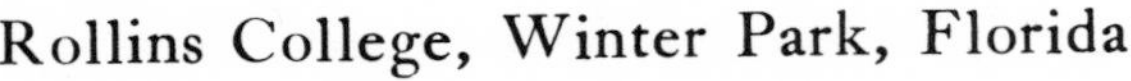

W · W · NORTON & COMPANY · INC · NEW YORK

Library of Congress Catalog Card No. 62-8635

Published simultaneously in the Dominion of Canada by George J. McLeod Limited, Toronto

PRINTED IN THE UNITED STATES OF AMERICA

Contents

Chapter Two The First Instruction Books and Singing Schools (1721–1764) 43

An Introduction to the Singing of Psalm-Tunes, John Tufts, 1726

The Grounds and Rules of Musick Explained, Thomas Walter, 1721

The Collections of William Tans'ur and Aaron Williams

A Collection of the Best Psalm Tunes, Josiah Flagg, 1764

Chapter Three The Music of the Ephrata Cloister and the Moravians 61

The Ephrata Cloister

Music of the Moravians

Chapter Four Native American Composers (1759–1810) 97

Chapter Eight Music of the Minstrel Shows 260

Chapter Nine National and Patriotic Songs (1794–1865) 279

Chapter Ten Romantic Ballads and Nationalist Composers 307

Illustrations

Between pages 246–247

Preface

THIS *Anthology* is designed for the use of all who are interested in the growth of music in America, the teacher, student, layman, scholar, and above all the performer. Between its covers are presented musical compositions spanning nearly 250 years, attesting to a surprising amount of activity in all media, and conceived within a periphery extending from Massachusetts to Georgia, Louisiana, and Ohio. Drawing from an extensive body of metrical psalms, psalm-settings, sacred and secular choral works, solo songs, keyboard pieces, opera, and music for small instrumental groups, the editors have endeavored to present a panorama of musical landmarks which have played an important part in the religious, social, and cultural life of our country.

The music, presented in an approximate chronology, has been selected on the basis of its artistic significance and musico-historical importance in American history from 1620 until the close of the Civil War in 1865. Special emphasis has been placed on music by native American composers. The problem of selection has been a thorny one. Some will question the absence of a piece particularly favored, and others will note that many compositions of undoubted merit and historical value have been omitted. No attempt has been made to include the music of "New Spain," folk music, tribal music of the American Indian, music of the Negro, Gospel songs, ragtime, blues, jazz, or the music of many religious sects, including the Shakers, Mennonites, Pietists, Dunkards, and others.

All the music in the *Anthology*, with the exception of the chapter devoted to the music of the Moravians, has been taken from the first or earliest available edition or manuscript or from photo copies of these sources. In no instance, with the exception noted above, have secondary sources been used. The date given under the title is, with exceptions, the date when the music first appeared in the form given.

The editors have endeavored to present the music as closely to the original as possible, retaining the original keys, dynamic indications, time signatures, note values, barring, and the order of the voices in part-music.

The original spelling and capitalization of the texts have been preserved, except for spelling out abbreviated words and substituting the modern "s" for "ſ." The often haphazard punctuation of the texts in the early music has been retained as far as practical, with additions and revisions provided when necessary to clarify the thought and phrasing. The psalm settings have the Protestant numbering.

To facilitate reading, the C-clef, frequently used in the early psalters and tunebooks, has been changed to the G-clef. The diamond-shaped notes of the early psalters and tunebooks, and the shape-notes used in Southern folk hymnody have been transcribed into conventional notation. Most of the homophonic part-music, which was originally written in open score, has been transcribed into close score, with the original voices carefully identified. When the voice parts are printed in score, a piano reduction with conventional time signatures has been provided.

Accidentals found in the original are placed before the note affected, and the few accidentals which were missing in the original have been placed above the notes. All corrections of misprints and doubtful notes have been indicated in footnotes. Slurs have been added in the vocal parts when omitted in the original version.

Two or more stanzas of the text have been included occasionally in order to give a better idea of the quality of the poetry, for purposes of comparison, or to complete the thought of the poem. The name of the composer is placed at the right of the title, and the name of the author of the text is usually placed at the end of each composition. The source of the music is given at the left of the title.

Finally, only complete compositions have been presented except in multi-movement works when, because of limitations of space, only one or two movements appear in the *Anthology*.

The commentaries are in no way intended to be a history of music in America or a detailed analysis of the music. It is the hope of the editors, however, that they will furnish sufficient background to stimulate extensive supplementary study. Biographical notes on the composers are included in the Appendix.

Those who wish to increase their knowledge and appreciation of early music in America will find available many books and periodicals with important scholarly contributions by leading authorities in the field. Books with general bibliographies include *America's Music* by Gilbert Chase (McGraw-Hill Book Co., New York); *American Music from 1620–1920* (Music Literature Outlines, Series III) by Harold Gleason (Levis Music Store, Rochester, New York); *The History of American Church Music* by Leonard Ellinwood (Morehouse-Gorham Co., New York); and *Our American Music* by John Tasker Howard (Thomas Y. Crowell, New York).

There remains the pleasant duty of acknowledging the aid of the many persons and institutions without whose co-operation this *Anthology* would never have become a reality.

We are especially grateful to Mr. Irving Lowens of the Music Division of the Library of Congress, who has followed the progress of this *Anthology* from the beginning and has been most generous with his help and advice, and to Dr. Donald M. McCorkle, Director of the Moravian Music Foundation, and Boosey and Hawkes, Inc. for making available the music of the Moravians.

Our sincere thanks also go to Dr. Leonard Ellinwood and the late Rev. Dr. Maurice Frost; to Dr. Harold Spivacke, Mr. Edward N. Waters, and Dr. Donald W. Krummel of the Music Division of the Library of Congress; Mr. Frank C. Campbell and Mr. Harold Merkleen of the New York Public Library; Dr. Ruth Watanabe and Miss Elizabeth Smith of the Sibley Music Library, University of Rochester; Dr. Wayne Barlow of the Eastman School of Music, University of Rochester; Dr. Zoltán Haraszti and Miss Ellen M. Oldham of the Boston Public Library; The Henry E. Huntington Library, San Marino, California; Mr. Stephen T. Riley, Massachusetts Historical Society, Boston; Dr. Brooks Shepard, Jr., Mr. George Nally, and Miss Reva B. Schwartz of the Yale University Library, New Haven, Connecticut; The Library Company of Philadelphia; Mrs. Marian Clarke and Mr. Donald B. Engley of the Watkinson Library, Trinity College, Hartford, Connecticut; Dr. Howard H. Peckham of the William L. Clements Library of American History and Dr. Allen P. Britton of the University of Michigan, Ann Arbor; The American Antiquarian Society, Worcester, Massachusetts; Mr. S. Foster Damon and Mr. David A. Jonah of the John Hay Library, Brown University, Providence, R.I.; The Johns Hopkins University Library, Baltimore, Maryland; The Rollins College Library, Winter Park, Florida; The Provost and Fellows of King's College, Cambridge, England; The Trustees of the British Museum; Mr. Walter Hinrichsen, President of the C. F. Peters Corporation; Mr. Wilbur Smith of the University of California, Special Collections Library, Los Angeles; and the Worcester Historical Society,

Worcester, Massachusetts.

We wish here to express our appreciation to Sig. Arturo Monzardo of Milan, Italy, for his painstaking work in copying the music.

Finally our sincere thanks go to Dr. Paul Henry Lang, and to Mr. Nathan Broder and other members of the staff of W. W. Norton & Company, and especially to Mr. Robert E. Farlow who realized the need for this *Anthology* and has followed its progress with patience and understanding.

W. Thomas Marrocco
Harold Gleason

June, 1963

MUSIC IN AMERICA

Chapter One

METRICAL PSALMODY IN NEW ENGLAND

1620-1720

The Ainsworth Psalter

Open wide in her lap lay the well-worn psalm-book of Ainsworth,
Printed in Amsterdam, the words and music together,
Rough-hewn, angular notes, like stones in the wall of a churchyard,
Darkened and overhung by the running vine of the verses.
The Courtship of Miles Standish by Henry Wadsworth Longfellow

DURING the first hundred years, the church music of the Puritans in America was confined to the unaccompanied unison singing of the metrical versions of the psalms as found in the various editions of the Ainsworth Psalter, the Sternhold and Hopkins Psalter, and the *Bay Psalm Book*. The more musically inclined Puritans doubtless sang psalm-tunes in harmony at home and possibly used some instrumental accompaniments. This is evinced by the fact that they knew, among others, Thomas Ravenscroft's psalter (1621), with the tunes "composed into 4. parts," and Richard Allison's psalter (1599) with the tune "to be sung and plaide vpon the Lute, Orpharyon, Citterne or Base Violl, seuerally or altogether, the singing part to be either Tenor or Treble to the Instrument, according to the nature of the voyce, or for fowre voyces."

When the Pilgrims left Delfthaven in 1620, on the first part of their journey to the New World, they brought with them a psalter prepared by the Biblical scholar, Henry Ainsworth (c. 1570–1623), for the use of the Puritan "Separatists" who had fled to Holland to escape religious intolerance. The title page of the Ainsworth Psalter reads as follows:

THE BOOK OF PSALMES: Englished both in Prose and Metre. *With Annotations, opening the words and sentences, by conference with other scriptures.* By *H. A.*
Ephe. 5.18.19.
Be ye filled with the Spirit: speaking to your selves in Psalms, and hymnes, and spiritual Songs: singing & making melodie in your hart to the Lord. Imprinted at Amsterdam, By GILES THORP. A°. D[i]. 1612.

The psalter contained 39 different melodies for the 150 psalms which Ainsworth set in meter. Ainsworth took the tunes from 16th-century English (Sternhold and Hopkins) and Dutch psalters, the latter being musically identical with the French.[1] The tunes selected for the *Anthology* were originally French (*Psalms 7, 8, 100*—Nos. 1, 2, 5), English (*Psalm 15*, No. 3), or German (*Psalm 34*, No. 4).

The tune used for *Psalm* 7 (No. 1) originally appeared in Calvin's first Psalter (Strasbourg, 1539), set to Clément Marot's French versification of *Psalm 130* (No. 1a). This psalter contained eighteen psalms, six with texts translated by Calvin, the remaining twelve by Marot. Ainsworth based his version of the tune on Sternhold and Hopkins, but divided the penultimate note in alternate lines in order to provide for the eight syllables in his text.

The famous tune for *Psalm 100*, known to all English-speaking people as "Old 100th," has been preserved intact from its first appearance in 1551 to the present time. It will, however, be noticed that the rhythmic pattern of the original tune, as set to *Psalm 134* (No. 5a), varies slightly from each of the other tunes. Other versions of *Psalm 100* may be found later in this chapter and in Chapter Two. The four-part setting of *Psalm 100* by William Parsons (No. 5b) is the first harmonization of the tune by an English composer. Parsons set William Kethe's well-known text which Kethe made in 1561 for the Anglo-Genevan Psalter by "Thomas Sterneholde and others." Of special interest regarding the use of instruments is the title of Parsons's psalter, which reads in part: "The whole Psalmes in foure partes, whiche may be song [*sic*] to al Musical instrumentes, set forth for the encrease of vertue: and aboleshyng of other vayne and triflyng ballades."

The versified texts of the psalms are almost invariably set with one note to a syllable, and the rhythm is binary. All the stanzas have the same meter and are sung to the same music, the psalm thus taking on the form of a hymn.

Fifteen different meters were employed by Ainsworth, stanzas with more than four lines and unusual meters predominating. Only one of his tunes is in short meter, and only two are in the four-line common meter in which most of the texts in the Sternhold and Hopkins Psalter and the *Bay Psalm Book* were set. The meter indicates the number of syllables in each line of the text. A table of the most usual meters is given below:

Short Meter	S.M. (6.6.8.6.)
Common Meter	C.M. (8.6.8.6.), also known as Ballad Meter
Common Meter Double	C.M.D. (8.6.8.6.8.6.8.6.) or (8.6.8.6. D.)
Long Meter	L.M. (8.8.8.8.)
Long Meter Double	L.M.D. (8.8.8.8.8.8.8.8.) or (8.8.8.8. D.)
Hallelujah Meter	H.M. (6.6.6.6.4.4.4.4.)

Six-line stanzas and irregular meters (sometimes called Particular or Peculiar Meter, P.M.) are usually designated by the number of syllables in each line, i.e. 6–8s (8.8.8.8.8.8.), 5–10s(10.10.10.10.), 10.10.11.11.

Most of the tunes in the Ainsworth Psalter are modal or quasi-modal. A few have definite major (Ionian) characteristics (*Psalm 8* and *Psalm 100*). *Psalm* 7 and *Psalm 34* are in the Dorian mode with a lowered sixth near the end of the tune. *Psalm 15*, with its narrow range,

[1] For detailed information on the early history of psalm-tunes consult *English & Scottish Psalm & Hymn Tunes, c. 1543–1677* (London, 1953) by Maurice Frost, *The Music of the French Psalter of 1562* (New York, 1939) by Waldo Selden Pratt, and *Grove's Dictionary of Music and Musicians*, article *Psalter* (5th edition, London and New York, 1954).

could be considered as being in either the Dorian or Aeolian mode.

A wide variety of rhythmic patterns is found throughout the psalter and in the tunes selected for the *Anthology*, and none of the melodies has the same note values throughout. Each line of the tunes in the *Anthology*, except *Psalm 15*, begins and ends with a long note. The tune for *Psalm* 7 has the same rhythmic pattern in lines 1, 3, 6, and 7 and in lines 2, 4, and 8, while line 5 is irregular. In *Psalm 8*, lines 1 and 4 and 2 and 5 are alike, while line 3 is irregular. *Psalm 15* is one of the two tunes in common meter and is unique in that it has a different rhythmic pattern for each line, and all lines but the first begin with a short note followed by a long note. Ainsworth has altered the equal-value notes of the original version of *Psalm 34* to an unusual pattern in which the second and third notes of each line are short (compare with *Psalm 85*, No. 10).

The Pilgrims at Plymouth are said to have been able to sing the long and sometimes complicated tunes from the music, without resorting to the practice of "lining-out" (singing by rote) which was used in the other Colonies. The melodies were all written in the C-clef in the range of men's voices, and Ainsworth suggested "that each people is to use the most grave, decent and comfortable manner of singing that they know."

The Ainsworth Psalter went through a number of editions, the last in 1690. It was used for a time in Salem and by the Pilgrims at Plymouth until they merged with the Massachusetts Bay Colony in 1692. The Pilgrims then adopted the *Bay Psalm Book* (1651), which was used by the Puritans of the Massachusetts Bay Colony. Thereafter the influence of the Ainsworth Psalter virtually disappeared, resulting in the loss of many fine tunes with longer stanzas and more melodic, rhythmic, and metrical variety than those found in the English Psalter (Sternhold and Hopkins), which favored four-line stanzas and common meter.

A number of the melodies chosen by Ainsworth for his versifications have, however, withstood the test of time and are found in many modern hymnals. The *Anthology* includes the tunes known today as *Old 124th* (*Psalm 8*), *Windsor* (*Psalm 15*), *Old 112th* (*Psalm 34*), and *Old 100th* (*Psalm 100*).

The *Bay Psalm Book* of 1640

> That soe wee may sing in Sion the Lords songs of prayse according to his owne will; untill hee take us from hence, and wipe away all our teares, & bid us enter into our masters ioye to sing eternall Halleluiahs.
>
> From John Cotton's Preface to the *Bay Psalm Book*, 1640

The Puritans who established the Massachusetts Bay Colony in 1628–1630 brought from England the Ravenscroft Psalter (London, 1621) and one of the many editions of the Sternhold and Hopkins Psalter (the first complete English edition was published in 1562). There was, however, in America as well as in England, a growing dissatisfaction with Sternhold and Hopkins's translations of the psalms, which many divines regarded as too far removed from the original Hebrew. As a result, a new and "faithful" metrical translation of the psalms was undertaken by thirty "pious and learned Ministers." Their efforts culminated in the *Bay Psalm Book* (as it came to be called), printed in Cambridge, Massachusetts, in 1640—the first book to be printed in British North America. It was soon adopted by most of the congregations in the Massachusetts Bay Colony, and exerted a strong influence on New England psalmody for the next hundred years. The title page of the *Bay Psalm Book* reads in part:

THE WHOLE BOOKE OF PSALMES *Faithfully* TRANSLATED *into* ENGLISH *Metre.* Whereunto is prefixed a discourse declaring not only the lawfullnes, but also the necessity of the heavenly Ordinance of singing Scripture Psalmes in the Churches of God. *Imprinted,* 1640.

At the end of the book, "An admonition to the Reader" names the tunes, drawn from the Ravenscroft and the Sternhold and Hopkins Psalters, that could be sung to the six meters of the psalms as follows:

The verses of these psalmes may be reduced to six kindes [meters], the first whereof may be sung in very neere fourty common tunes; as they are collected, out of our chief musicians, by *Tho. Ravenscroft.*
The second kinde may be sung in three tunes as *Ps.* 25. 50. & 67. in our english psalm books. [Sternhold and Hopkins]
The third. may be sung indifferently, as *ps.* the 51. 100. & ten commandements, in our english psalme books. which three tunes [meters] aforesaid, comprehend almost all this whole book of psalmes, as being tunes [meters] most familiar to us.
The fourth. as *ps.* 148. of which there are but about five.
The fift. as *ps.* 112. or the *Pater noster,* of which there are but two. *viz.* 85. & 138.
The sixt. as *ps.* 113, of which but one, *viz.* 115.

The use of only six meters in the metrical psalms of the *Bay Psalm Book* (1640), with the heavy emphasis on common meter, resulted, as has been pointed out, in the loss of the wide variety of tunes found in the Ainsworth Psalter. There were also single examples of eleven other meters in the Sternhold and Hopkins Psalter which were not retained. One hundred and twelve of the psalms in the *Bay Psalm Book* are in common meter, fourteen in short meter, fifteen in long meter, six in Hallelujah meter, two in 6–8s, and one in 12–8s. Examples of tunes in each of these six meters are given in the *Anthology*, following the order of the above "Admonition."

Yorke (*York*) is one of the 39 harmonized tunes in common meter included in the Ravenscroft Psalter (London, 1621), the first source mentioned in the "Admonition." As was customary in part-music, the tunes were placed in the tenor. They were named (many for the first time by Ravenscroft) after English cathedral and university towns or after various localities with which the tunes were especially identified. The Ravenscroft Psalter contained 105 four-part settings by some of England's most accomplished musicians. Among them were Allison (Alison), Dowland (Douland), Farnaby, Morley, Tallis, Tomkins, John Milton, Sr. (father of the poet), and Ravenscroft himself. The use of the mensural notation sign for Imperfect Time and Perfect Prolation in Milton's setting of *York* (No. 6) is characteristic of Ravenscroft's effort to preserve an already obsolete practice. Milton's harmonization is characterized by three cadences on the dominant, a striking modal progression at the beginning of the third line, and an effective final cadence. The text of the versification of *Psalm 73*, taken from the *Bay Psalm Book* (1640), is set beneath Milton's text as it might have been sung by the Puritans. The original version of *York* is also given (No. 6a) as it is found in the Scottish Psalter (1615), where it is called *The Stilt*, obviously because of the alternating skips in the melody. The tune, with the B-natural in the second line, appears in a two-part setting in the *Bay Psalm Book* (1698), and it has maintained its popularity up to the present time.

The simple, chant-like melody of *Psalm 7* (No. 7) moves above the key-note within a range of a fifth. It will be noted that the first and third lines have an unusual rhythmic pattern. The tune first appeared in the Ravenscroft Psalter, where it is called *Canterbury*.

Sternhold and Hopkins's version of the tune for *Psalm 100* (No. 8) follows the rhythmic pattern used in the Parsons Psalter (1563) and varies only in the last line from the French-Genevan Psalter (1551; *Anthology*, Nos. 5b and 5a).

The versifications of the six psalms in Hallelujah meter in the *Bay Psalm Book* were all sung to the tune for *Psalm 148* (No. 9) as found in the Sternhold and Hopkins Psalter —the only psalm in that meter. The last five lines in *Psalm 148* have varied rhythmic patterns, and the use of a B-flat in the fourth and sixth lines is also of special interest.

Psalm 85 (No. 10) is set to the tune that Sternhold and Hopkins used for the metrical version of the *Lord's Prayer*. The melody also appeared in the Ainsworth Psalter (*Psalm 34*) in the Dorian mode (*Anthology*, No. 4). The use of accidentals in lines 3 and 4 in the Sternhold and Hopkins version, however, has given the tune a tonal character. It will also be noticed that the rhythmic pattern varies from Ainsworth's version.

The sixth meter (12–8s) is represented by only one psalm in Sternhold and Hopkins (*Psalm 113*) and one in the *Bay Psalm Book* (*Psalm 115;* No. 11). This striking tune, known in Germany as early as 1526, was used by Calvin in his first psalter of 1539 and entered the repertory of German chorales as *O Mensch, bewein' dein' Sünde gross*. The tune was also a famous battle-song of the French Huguenots and became known as the "Huguenot Marseillaise." Ainsworth set his version of *Psalm 84* and *Psalm 136* to this tune; the latter psalm, however, required a change in meter from 8.8.8.8.8.8.D. to 8.8.7.8.8.7.D.

The title page of the *Bay Psalm Book* (1640) includes a quotation from James 5: "*If any be afflicted, let him pray, and if any be merry let him sing psalmes.*" The Puritans followed this admonition with enthusiasm and sang their psalms with "a lively voyce." There were some, however, who objected to the melodies made by "sinful men" and called the tunes "Genevah Gigs."

"Lining-out" of the psalms, already practiced in England, was recommended in 1647 by John Cotton "as a necessary helpe," except "where all have books and can reade, or else can say the *Psalme* by heart." "Lining-out" was also applied to psalm-singing, and a deacon or elder would "set the tune" at the proper pitch (if he could) and sing the psalm one line at a time, the congregation repeating what he had just sung. The lack of deacons with a good sense of pitch and an ear for music was one of the contributing factors in the gradual deterioration of congregational singing.

The *Bay Psalm Book* of 1698

> Let the word of God dwell in you richly in all wisdom, teaching and admonishing one another in Psalms, Hymns and spiritual Songs, singing to the Lord with grace in your hearts. Colossians 3:16
>
> From the title page of the *Bay Psalm Book*, ninth edition, 1698.

In spite of the popular acceptance of the *Bay Psalm Book* of 1640 and the reprint of 1647, "persons of culture" thoroughly disapproved of the many crude and awkward "close-fitting" metrical translations made by pious men who they felt had little, if any, ability as poets. The demand for metrical psalms that would be more singable and of greater literary value led to the publication of a third edition of the *Bay Psalm Book* in 1651.

This "revised and refined" edition was largely the work of the Rev. Henry Dunster, first president of Harvard College. The poetry was improved, new versifications were made, and alternate versions of some psalms were added. A new title page was given the book, and a number of hymns and spiritual songs (found in English psalters) were included for the first time in the *Bay Psalm Book*.

The 1651 edition of the *Bay Psalm Book* (known also as the *New England Psalm Book*) was enthusiastically received. It became the definitive version for over one hundred years and went through many editions here as well as in England and Scotland. Only the metrical versions of Sternhold and Hopkins, Tate and Brady, Isaac Watts, and the Scottish Psalter exceeded it in the number of editions, or in long-continued use.

The first known edition of the *Bay Psalm Book* to include music was the ninth, published in Boston in 1698. Its title, identical in text with the 1651 edition, reads:

THE PSALMS HYMNS, AND SPIRITUAL SONGS, OF THE Old & New Testament: Faithfully Translated into *English Meetre*. For the use, Edification and Comfort of the Saints in publick and private, especially in *New-England* . . . . *Boston*, Printed by *B. Green*, and *J. Allen*, for *Michael Perry*, under the West-End of the Town house. 1698.

Irving Lowens has shown that the music included in the *Bay Psalm Book* of 1698 is identical with that in the 1674 and 1679 editions of John Playford's *Introduction to the Skill of Music* (London). He has also made a strong case for the possibility that a missing edition of the *Bay Psalm Book* with music was published in England between 1689 and 1691, and that the *Bay Psalm Book* of 1698 may have been an American reprint of that edition.[2]

The thirteen tunes added at the back of the book appear in the following order: *Oxford* (C.M.), *Lichfield* [*sic*] (C.M.), *Low Dutch* (C.M.), *York* (C.M.), *Windsor* (C.M.), *Cambridge Short* (S.M.), *St. Davids* (C.M.), *Martyrs* (C.M.), *Hackney* (C.M.), *Psalm 119* (C.M.D.), *Psalm 100* (L.M.), *Psalm 115* (12–8s), *Psalm 148* (H.M.).

The large proportion of common meter versifications in the *Bay Psalm Book* (there were 125 in the 1651 edition) is reflected in the fact that nine of the thirteen tunes in the 1698 edition are in common meter (one of these is C.M.D.). It will also be noticed that short meter, long meter, 12–8s, and Hallelujah meter are represented by one tune each and that there is no tune given for 6–8s, although one is provided for in the 1640 edition (*Anthology*, No. 10).

The tunes are all set in two parts, treble and bass, without a text but with the number of a psalm in appropriate meter indicated. The letters F[a], S[ol], L[a], M[i], known as "fasola" notation, are placed under the diamond-shaped notes. This notation is identical with that used by Playford in his *Introduction to the Skill of Music* (London, 1672).

Six of the tunes from the *Bay Psalm Book*, 1698, are included in this section of the *Anthology*. Four of the seven remaining tunes may be found in the present volume—*Windsor* (*Psalm 15* in Ainsworth; No. 3); *Yorke* [*sic*] and *Psalm 115* (Nos. 6, 11); and *Litchfield* (*London Tune* in Walter; No. 24). The melodies of *London Tune* (*Litchfield*) and *Yorke* are identical with those in the *Bay Psalm Book* of 1698; *Windsor* and *Psalm 115* have been slightly altered. The tunes must have been well known to the Puritans, since they could all be found in the Sternhold and Hopkins or the Ravenscroft Psalters, and their quality and durability are attested to by the fact that at least nine of the thirteen tunes are to be found in modern hymnals.

The rhythmic patterns show considerable variety. All six tunes, except *Psalm 100* (No. 15), have one or more lines that begin with a short note. A few tunes have regular patterns for the first half of the tune and irregular patterns for the second half. All have common-time signatures, except *Martyrs*, which is in triple time.

Four of the six tunes given in the *Anthology* lie within the range of an octave (*Martyrs, Psalm 100*) or ninth (*Psalm 119*, No. 16; *Psalm 148*, No. 17), while the remaining two tunes have a compass of a fourth (*Low Dutch*, No. 13), or fifth (*Oxford*, No. 12). Most of

[2] Irving Lowens, "The Bay Psalm Book in 17th-Century New England," *Journal of the American Musicological Society*, VII (1955), 28.

the six tunes are modal or quasi-modal. *Martyrs* (No. 14) is in the Dorian mode; *Psalm 100* is in the Ionian (major) mode. *Oxford* is unusual in that it begins on the raised seventh degree. It was originally a Scottish tune in the Dorian mode with F-natural throughout. *Low Dutch* first appeared in Thomas East's *Whole Booke of Psalmes* (1592), harmonized in the Ionian mode. *Psalm 148* varies slightly from the version in Sternhold and Hopkins (No. 9). Modulations occur in *Psalm 119* and *Psalm 148*.

The section in the *Bay Psalm Book* that contains the music begins with "some few directions for ordering the Voice in Setting these following Tunes of the Psalms." The Preface, borrowed from Playford's *Brief Introduction to the Skill of Musick* (London, 1667) continues with the following often-quoted passage intended as an aid to the deacon in selecting the initial pitch:

> First observe of how many *Notes* compass the *Tune* is. Next, the place of your first *Note;* and how many *Notes* above & below that: so as you may begin the *Tune* of your first *Note* as the rest may be sung in the compass of your and the peoples voices, without *Squeaking* above, or *Grumbling* below. . . .

The Preface names *Oxford, Litchfield* (also known as *London*), *Low Dutch, York, Windsor,* and *Cambridge Short* as tunes in which "the first note will bear a cheerful high pitch"; for *St. Davids, Martyrs, Hackney* (also known as *St. Mary's*), *Psalm 119, Psalm 115,* and *Psalm 148* "begin your first note low"; for *Psalm 100,* with the first note about in the middle of the compass, "begin your first note indifferently high," that is, not too low.

The New Version

> The Lord Bishop of London, in 1698, "persuaded that it [the *New Version*] may take off that unhappy objection which has hitherto lain against the Singing Psalms . . . heartily recommended the Use of this Version to all his Brethren within his Diocess."
>
> A maid in the household of Tate's brother refused, however, to sing the new psalms saying: "If you must know the plain truth, sir, as long as you sung Jesus Christ's psalms I sung along with ye; but now that you sing psalms of your own invention, ye may sing by yourselves."
>
> *Three Centuries of American Hymnody* by Henry Wilder Foote

During the 17th century there was a growing desire in England, and to some extent in America, for more fluent and poetic metrical translations of the psalms, and many freer versions began to appear. These culminated in 1696 with the publication in London of the *New Version of the Psalms of David, fitted to the tunes used in churches* by Nahum Tate (1652–1715), Poet Laureate and librettist for Henry Purcell's opera *Dido and Aeneas,* and Nicholas Brady (1659–1726), an Anglican divine. The Sternhold and Hopkins Psalter soon became known as the "Old Version" and the Tate and Brady as the "New Version." The two existed in the English church side by side, until eventually they were lost in the hymn-like psalmody and hymnody of the non-conformist divine, Isaac Watts (1674–1748), and later writers. Music was not included in the first edition of the *New Version* of 1696, but in 1700 *A Supplement to the New Version* was issued with a few tunes. The important sixth edition (1708) included 75 tunes set in two parts.

The congregations in New England were partial to the *Bay Psalm Book,* which had 27 editions there before 1762; and the *New Version* had little influence in America until the middle of the 18th century. However, King's Chapel in Boston, an Episcopal church, adopted the *New Version* as early as 1713, and in the same year an edition including nine tunes was published there. In 1720 Samuel Sewall noted in his *Diary* that, at a meeting in the schoolhouse, they "sang four times out of Tate and Brady." The Baptists in Boston changed to the *New Version* in 1740, and gradually it was accepted in other localities, particularly in the Episcopal churches.

The *Supplement to the New Version* introduced to America some of our finest hymn tunes, among them *St. Anne's* (No. 18) and *Winchester* (*Winchester Old*). The former, known today by Watts's text "O God, our help in ages past," is ascribed to William Croft, organist of St. Anne's in Soho, London. It first appeared anonymously in the *Supplement* (1708), where it is set to Nahum Tate's well-known versification of *Psalm 42.* The tune for the *Song of the Angels* (No. 19) had its origin in Thomas East's *Whole Booke of Psalmes* (1592) and was named *Winchester* by Ravenscroft in his psalter of 1621. Nahum Tate's paraphrase of the Biblical text from Luke 2 is one of our best-known Christmas hymns.

In 1755 Thomas Johnston published in Boston a tune supplement to the *New Version* containing, possibly for the first time in America, a three-part setting of the famous tune *Mear.* This tune made its initial appearance (under the title *Middlesex*) in Simon Browne's *A Sett of Tunes in 3 Parts* (London, 1720). It will be noted that Johnston's version of the tune (No. 20) varies from Browne's (No. 20a) only in the last two measures of the first line, and that the tune is in the tenor in Browne's setting. A distinguishing characteristic of the melody is the sudden shift in the rhythmic pattern in the penultimate measure of the second and fourth lines. *Mear* was not only a favorite 18th-century tune, but it became one of the popular tunes in 19th-century Southern folk hymnody and may also be found in many modern hymnals.

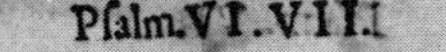

16 Psalm. VI. VII.

V. 6. for in the death &c.] This doctrine, King Hezekiah explayneth thus; for hell not confess thee, death shal not prayse thee; they that goe down the pit, shal not hope for truth: the living the living, he shal confess thee as I doo this day: thee father to the children make-knowne thy truth. Isa. 38. 18. 19. So after, in Psal. 115. 17. 18. hel] or the grave deadlyshed; the place or state of the dead. See the note on Psal. 16, 10. confess] or thanks, celebrate, divulge or freely publish with praise and comendation. This same word also used for confessing of synns; Psal. 32. 5.

V. 7. I faynt.] or am over-yawed with my sighing; the like speech Baruch useth, Jer. The original word iagaghn, signifieth yawing, toyl, turmoil and sore labour, of body or mind and consequently, fainting, through wearynes: and is opposed to rest or quietnes: Lam. every night] or, the whole night. I water] that is, baeth, or dissolve into water I melt my bedsted. These are extensive figurative speeches, to expres the greatnes of his sorow. In the Hebrue they are also in the future time, I shal melt; I shal make swim; that usually melt and baeth; noting the continuance of his affliction.

V. 8. myne eye] This may be taken for the whole face or visage; as in Num. 11. 7. the eye is used for the colour or appearance. gnawen] The Hebrue Ghnashash is to gnaw, fret, and so to make deformed and ugly, and to consume. Herof Ghnash is a moth-worm, Psal. 39. 12. that fretteth garments. A like speech Job useth, myne eye is dimmed with indignation Job. 17. 7. but gnawen, here is a word more vehement. So after in Psal. 31. 10. 11. indignation] for greif that I take being provoked by the enemies.

V. 11. let be abasht] or, shal be abasht; The Hebrue Bosh, signifieth to be abasht, wax pale and wann; as when the colour fadeth and withereth; and noteth both disappointment of expectation, Job. 6. 20. and confusion or destruction. Jer. 48. 1, 20. let them return or, recoyl: a signe also of discomfiture and shame. so Psal. 56. 10. in a moment] or minute: that is, a short space, or suddaynly.

Psalm. 7.

1. Shigajon, of David: which he sang to Iehovah; upon the words of Cush, son of Iemini.

2. IEhovah my God, in thee I hope for-safetie: save-thou me from al that-persecute me, & deliver-thou me.

3. Least he tear-in-peeces like a Lion my soul: breaking, while ther is none delivering.

4. Iehovah my God, if I have doon this: if there-be injurious-evil in my palms,

Psalm. 7.

2. IEhovah mine almightie-God, I hope in thee: save me from al that me pursue, and deliver mee. 3. Least he a renting-Lion my sowl in peeces-tear: breaking-asunder, while ther is no-one deliverer.

4. Iehovah mine almighty-God, if this-thing doon have I, if that, ther be within my palmes wrongful-iniquitie,

Psalm. VII. 17

5. If I have rewarded, evil to him-that-had-peace-with-me: (yea I have-released, my distresser without cause:)

6. Let the enemy pursue my sowl, and take it; and tread-down my life on the earth: and my glorie, let him make-it-dwel, in the dust Selah.

7. Rise-up, Iehovah, in thy anger; be thou lifted-up, for the rages of my distressers: & wake-thou-up-unto me, judgement thou-hast-commanded.

8. And the congregation of peoples, shall compasse-thee-about: and for it, return thou to the high-place.

9. Iehovah, wil judge the peoples: judge-thou me Iehovah; according-to my justice, and according-to my perfection in me.

10. Oh let the malice of the wicked, be at-an-end, and stablish thou the just: for thou triest the harts, and reins, just God.

11. My sheild is in God: the saviour, of the right in hart.

12. God is a just judge: and God angerly-threatneth, every day.

13. If he-turn not, he wil whet his sword: he hath bent his bow, and made it ready.

14. And for him, he-hath made-ready the instruments of death: his arrowes, he-worketh for the hot-persecutors.

15. Loe he shalbe-in-travel of painful-iniquitie: for he hath conceived molestation, and shal bring-forth a lye.

16. He hath digged a pit, and delved it: and is-fallen, into the corrupting-ditch he wrought.

5. If I have him rewarded yll,
that with mee was at-peace:
(yea him that my distresser was
causless, I did release.)

6. Let foe pursue my sowl, and take
and tread my life on clay:
my glorie also let him make-
dwel, in the dust. Selah.

7. Rise-up, Iehovah, in thy wrath;
for rages of my foes,
be thou lift-up: and wake to me,
judgement thou-diddst propose.

8. And round-about thee compass shal,
the peoples assembly:
and for the same, doo thou return
unto the place-on-hye.

9. Iehovah, wil the peoples judge:
Iehovah judge thou me;
even-as my justice is, and as
my perfectnes in me.

10. Oh let the wickeds malice, end,
and stablish-thou-firmly
the just-man: for, o just God, thou
the harts and reins doost-try.

11. My sheild in God; the saviour,
of the upright in hart.

12. God, is a just judge: and ech day,
God, angry-threatneth smart.

13. For if that he doo not return,
his sword he sharp wil whett:
his bow he bended hath; and he
the same hath ready-sett.

14. And for him, he hath ready-made
the instruments of death:
for them that hotly-persecute,
his arrowes he worketh.

15. Loe he shalbe in travel of
painful-iniquitie:
for molestation he conceivd,
and shal bring forth a lye.

16. A hollow-pit he digged hath,
and delved-deep the same:
and falln he is, into the ditch
that he did working-frame.

C 17

Psalme 7 from the Ainsworth Psalter (Amsterdam, 1612).
By courtesy of the Trustees of the Boston Public Library.
See No. 1, p. 24.

1. PSALME 7 (C.M.D.)

1612

The Book of Psalmes
Henry Ainsworth
(*Amsterdam, 1612*)

Henry Ainsworth
(c. 1570–1623)

1a. PSALME 130 (7.6.7.6.D.)

1539

Aulcuns pseaulmes et cantiques
Calvin's First Psalter
(*Strasbourg, 1539*)

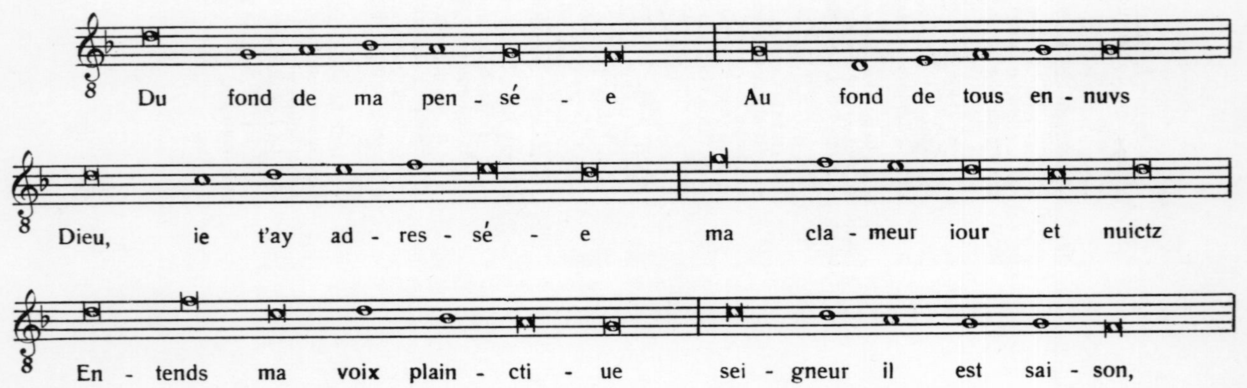

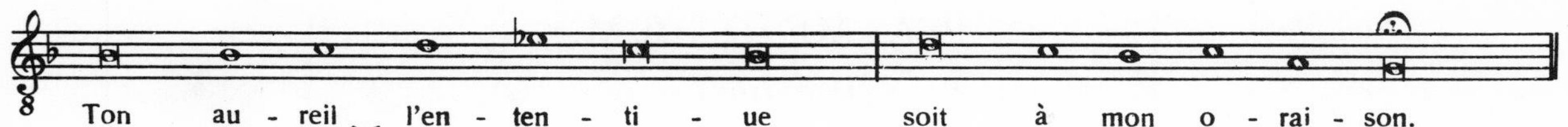

Clément Marot
(1496–1544)

Note: This is *Psalm 129* in the Catholic system of numbering.

2. PSALME 8 (10.10.10.10.10.)

(*Old 124th*)

1551

The Book of Psalmes
Henry Ainsworth
(*Amsterdam, 1612*)

Louis Bourgeois
(c. 1510–c. 1561)

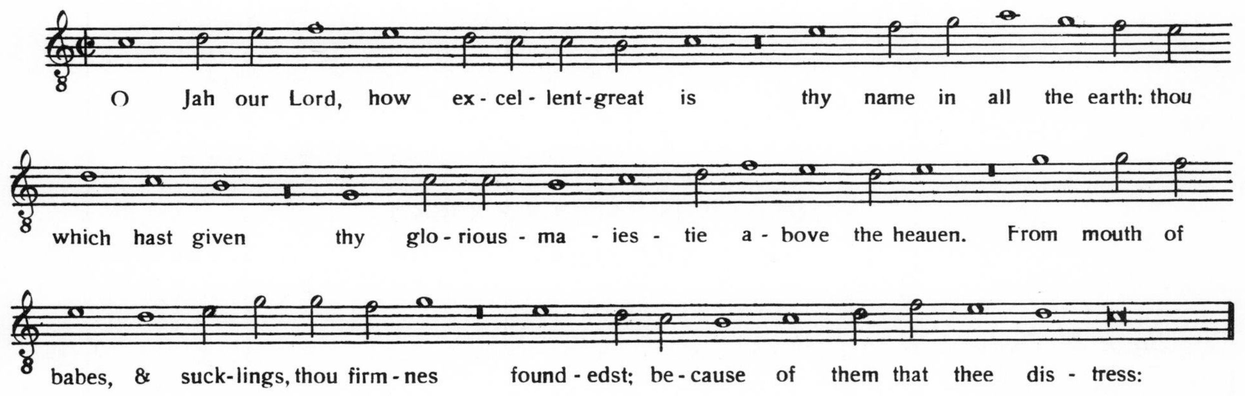

2

To make the foe, and self-avenger cease:
When I behold thy heav'ns, thy fingers deed:
the moon and starrs, which thou hast stablished.
What is frayl-man that him thou remembrest?
and Adams son, that him thou visitest?

3

For thou a little lesser hast made him,
than be the Gods: and crownd him with glorie
and-eke with honourable-decencie.
Of thy hand-works, thou gavest him ruling:
under his feet, thou set didst every-thing.

4

Sheep & beeves all: and feild beasts with the same.
Fowl of the heav'ns, fish of the sea also:
that through the path-wayes of the seas dooth go.
O Jah our Lord: how excellent-great-fame
in all the earth hath thy renouned-name.

Henry Ainsworth
(c. 1570–1623)

3. PSALME 15 (C.M.)

(*Windsor*)

1591

The Book of Psalmes
Henry Ainsworth
(*Amsterdam, 1612*)

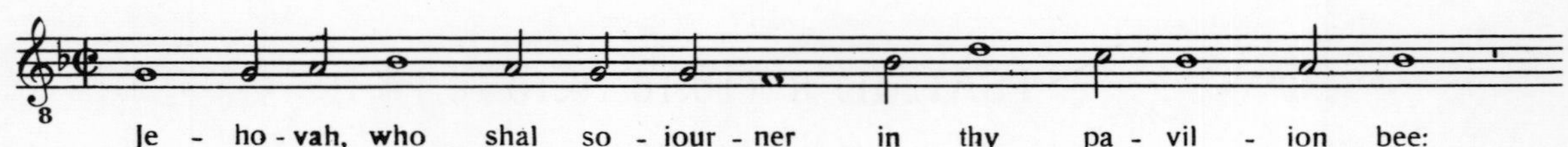

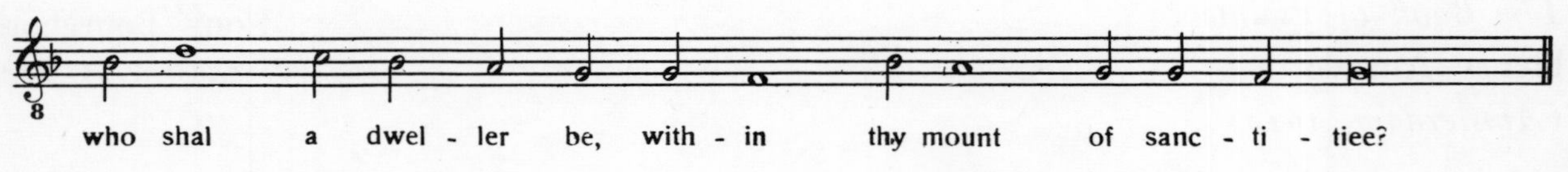

Henry Ainsworth
(c. 1570–1623)

4. PSALME 34 (8.8.8.8.8.8.)

(*Old 112th*)

1539

The Book of Psalmes
Henry Ainsworth
(*Amsterdam, 1612*)

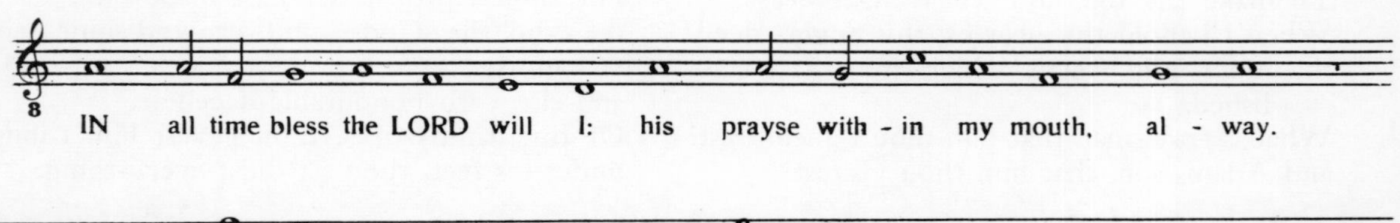

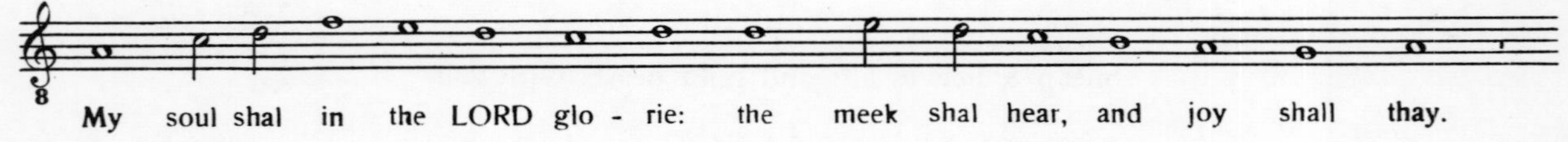

Henry Ainsworth
(c. 1570–1623)

5. PSALME 100 (L.M.)

1551

The Book of Psalmes
Henry Ainsworth
(*Amsterdam, 1612*)

Louis Bourgeois
(c. 1510–c. 1561)

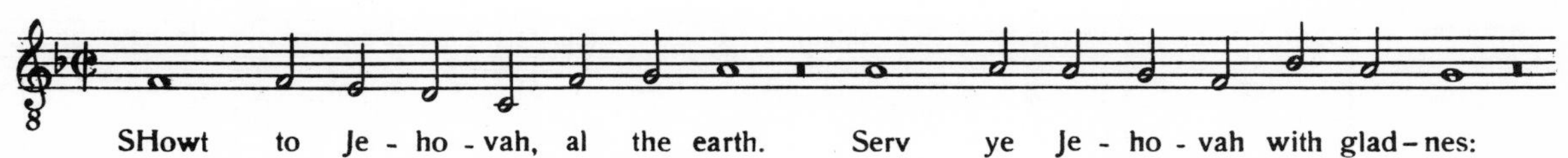

2
Its he that made us, and not wee;
his folk, and sheep of his feeding.
O with confession enter yee
his gates, his courtyards with praising:

3
confess to him, bless ye his name.
Because Jehovah he good is:
his mercy ever is the same:
and his faith, unto al ages.

Henry Ainsworth
(c. 1570–1623)

5a. PSEAUME CXXXIV (L.M.)

1551

Trente quatre pseaumes
French-Genevan Psalter
(*Geneva, 1551*)

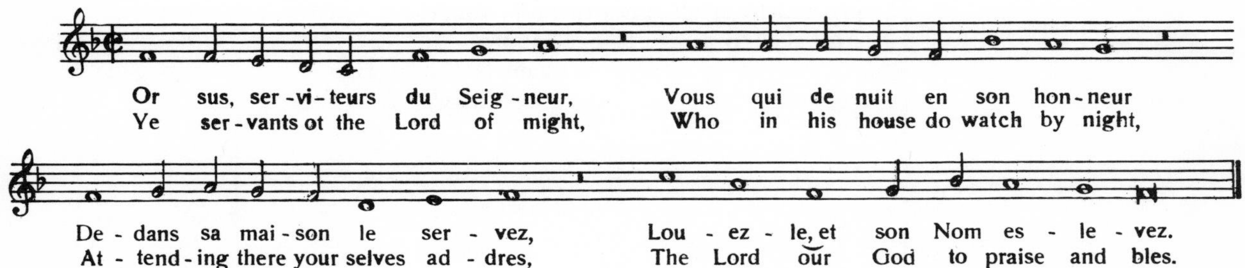

Théodore de Bèze
(1519–1605)

5b. PSALME C (L.M.)

1563

The Whole Psalmes in Foure Partes,
Parsons's Psalter
(*London, 1563*)

William Parsons
(16th century)

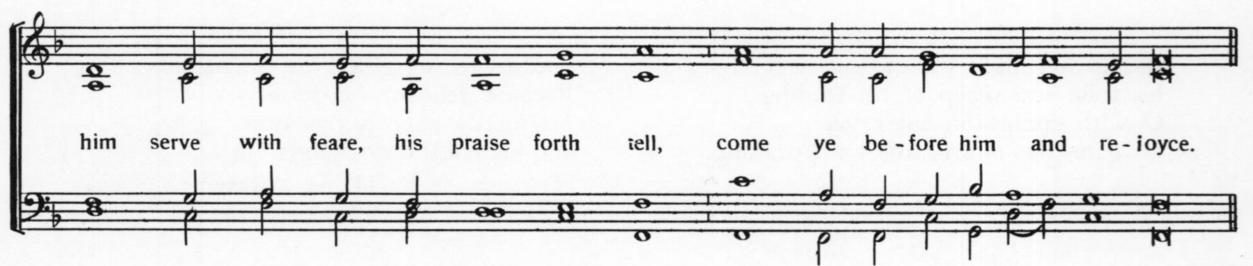

2
The Lord, ye knowe, is God in dede:
Without our aide, he did us make:
We are his folke: he doeth us fede.
And for his shepe, he doeth us take.

3
Oh, entre then his gates with praise:
Approche with ioye, his courtes unto
Praise, laude, and blesse his name alwayes
For it is semely so to do.

4
For why? the Lord our God is good:
His mercie is for euer sure:
His trueth at all times firmely stoode
And shal from age to age indure.

William Kethe
(16th century)

6. YORKE TUNE (C.M.)

A Prayer to the Holy Ghost

1621

The Whole Booke of Psalmes
Thomas Ravenscroft
(*London, 1621*)

John Milton, Sr.
(c. 1563–1647)

The alternate stanza (1.) is taken from
Ps. 73: *Bay Psalm Book*, 1640.

6a. THE STILT (C.M.)

1615

The CL. Psalmes of David
Scottish Psalter
(*Edinburgh, 1615*)

7. PSALME 7 (S.M.)

1621

Sternhold and Hopkins Psalter
Psalme 25
(*London, 1624*)

Ps. 7: *Bay Psalm Book*, 1640

8. PSALME 100 (L.M.)

1551

Sternhold and Hopkins Psalter
Psalme 100
(*London, 1624*)

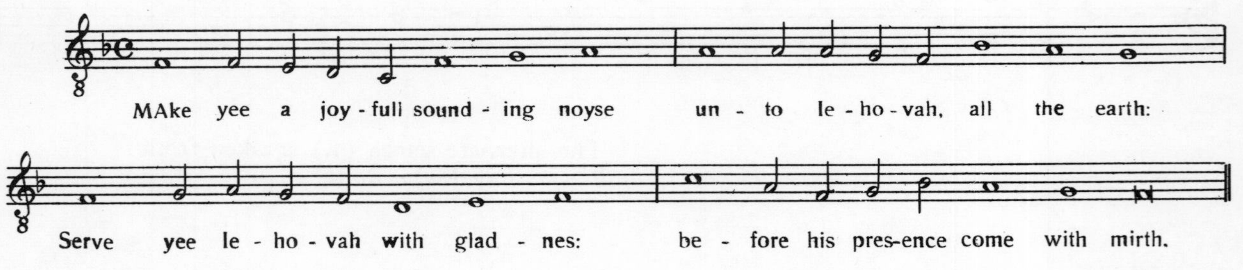

2
Know, that Iehovah he is God,
who hath us formed it is hee,
& not our selves: his owne people
& sheepe of his pasture are wee.

3
Enter into his gates with prayse,
into his Courts with thankfullness:
make yee confession unto him,
& his name reverently blesse.

4
Because Iehovah he is good,
for evermore is his mercy:
& unto generations all
continue doth his verity.

Ps. 100: *Bay Psalm Book*, 1640

9. PSALME 148 (H.M.)

Hallelujah

1558

Sternhold and Hopkins Psalter
Psalme 148
(*London, 1624*)

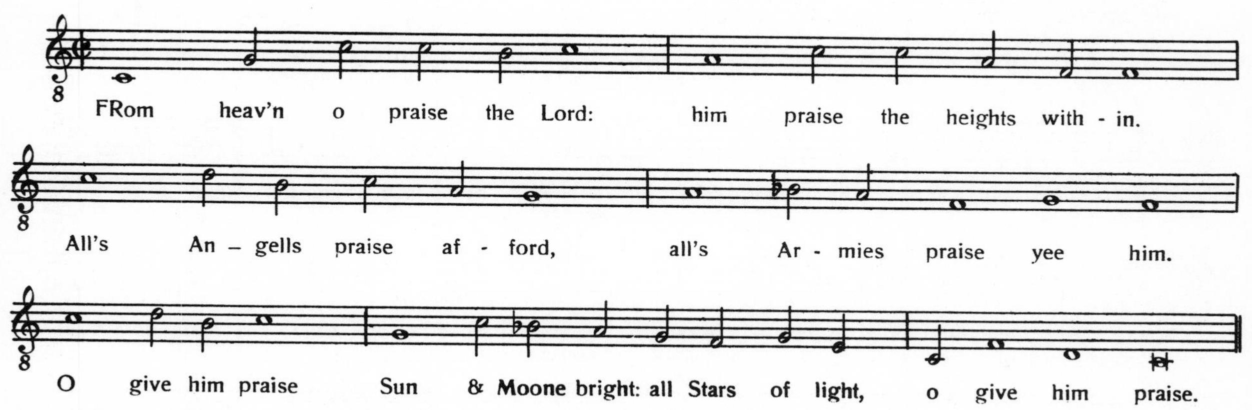

Ps. 148: *Bay Psalm Book*, 1640

10. PSALME 85 (6-8s)

1539

Sternhold and Hopkins Psalter
Pater noster
(*London, 1624*)

Ps. 85: *Bay Psalm Book*, 1640

11. PSALME 115 (12-8s)

1556

Sternhold and Hopkins Psalter
Psalme 113
(*London, 1624*)

2

Noses have they, but doe not smell.
Hands have they, but cannot handell,
  feet have they but doe not go:
And through their throat they never spake.
Like them are they, that doe them make:
  & all that trust in them are so.
Trust to the Lord O Israell,
He is their help, their shield as well.
  O Arons house the Lord trust yee:
Hee is their help, & hee their shield.
Who fear the Lord, trust to him yield:
  their help also their shield is hee.

Ps. 115: *Bay Psalm Book*, 1640

12. OXFORD TUNE (C.M.)

1564

Bay Psalm Book
(Boston, 1698)

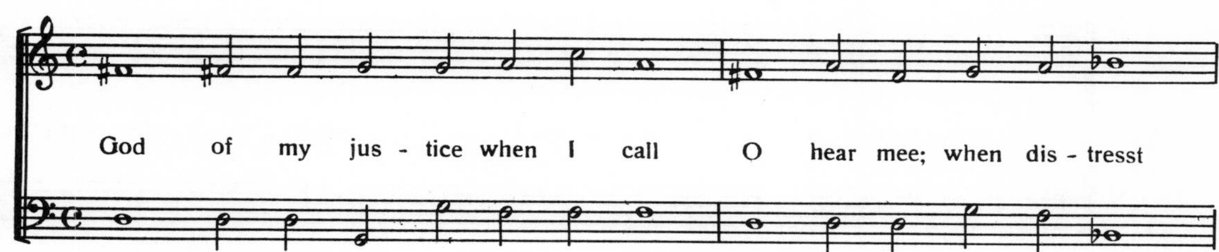

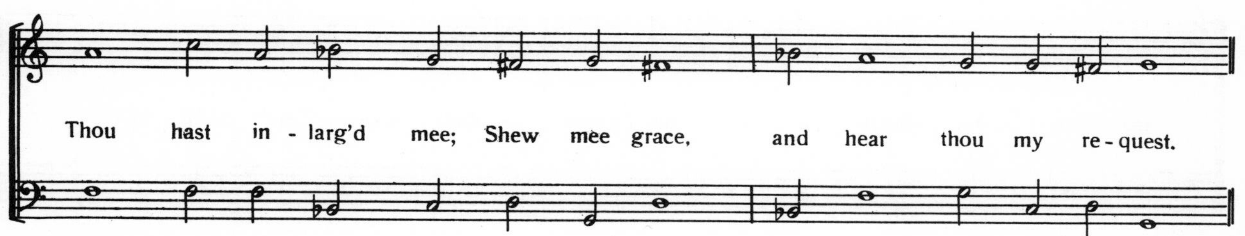

2
Ye sons of men my glory turn
to shame how long will you?
How long will yee love vanitie
and still deceit pursue?

3
But know the LORD hath set apart
for him his gracious saint;
The LORD will hear when unto him
I pour out my complaint.

4
Be stirred up; but do not sinn
consider seriously
Within your heart, with silence deep
when on your bed you lie.

5
The sacrifice of righteousness
let sacrificed bee;
And confidently put your trust
upon the LORD do yee.

Ps. 4: *Bay Psalm Book*, 1698

Note: The dates given for the music in Nos. 12–17 are the dates when the tunes were first published. The two-part settings first appeared in John Playford's *Introduction*, 1674.

13. LOW DUTCH TUNE (C.M.)

1592

Bay Psalm Book
(Boston, 1698)

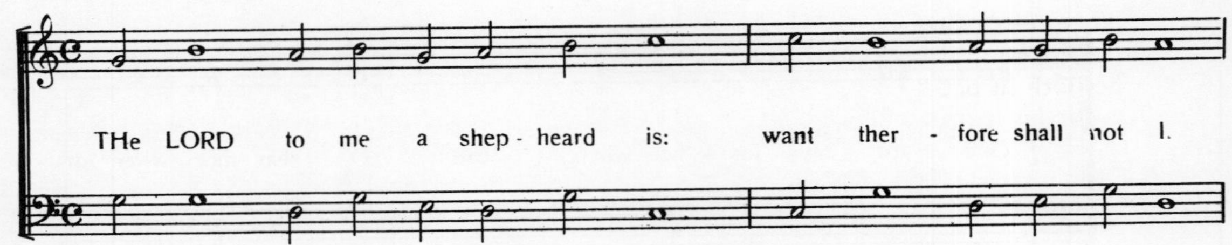

2
Hee leads mee to the waters still.
Restore my soul doth hee:
In paths of righteousness, he will
for his names sake lead mee.

3
In valley of deaths shade although
I walk I'le fear none ill:
For thou with me thy rod, also
thy staff me comfort will.

4
Thou hast 'fore me a table spread,
in presence of my foes:
Thou dost anoint with oyle my head,
my cup it ouer-flowes.

5
Goodness and mercy my dayes all
shall surely follow mee:
And in the LORDs house dwell I shall
so long as dayes shall bee.

Ps. 23: *Bay Psalm Book*, 1698

Note: The above version of *Psalm 23* is identical with that in the 1651 edition of the *Bay Psalm Book*.

1

The Lord to mee a shepheard is,
want therefore shall not I.
Hee in the folds of tender-grasse,
doth cause mee downe to lie:

2

To waters calme me gently leads
Restore my soule doth hee:
he doth in paths of righteousnes:
for his names sake leade mee.

3

Yea through in valley of death's shade
I walk, none ill I'le feare:
because thou art with mee, thy rod,
and staffe my comfort are.

4

For mee a table thou hast spread,
in presence of my foes:
thou dost annoynt my head with oyle,
my cup it over-flowes.

5

Goodnes & mercy surely shall
all my dayes follow mee:
and in the Lords house I shall dwell
so long as dayes shall bee.

Ps. 23: *Bay Psalm Book*, 1640

14. MARTYRS TUNE (C.M.)

1615

Bay Psalm Book
(*Boston, 1698*)

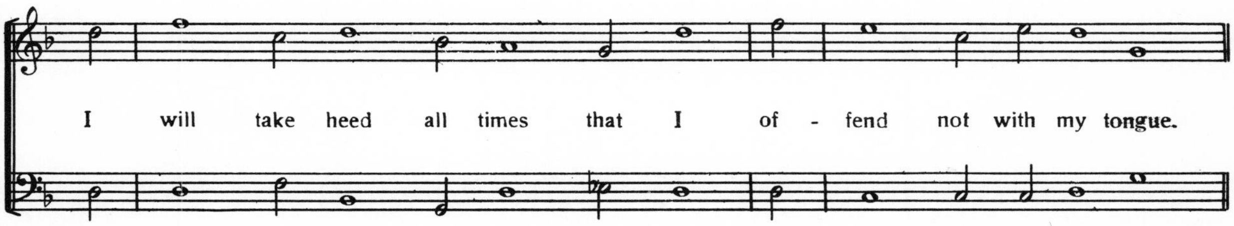

Ps. 39: *Bay Psalm Book*, 1698

15. PSALM 100 (L.M.)

1551

Bay Psalm Book
(Boston, 1698)

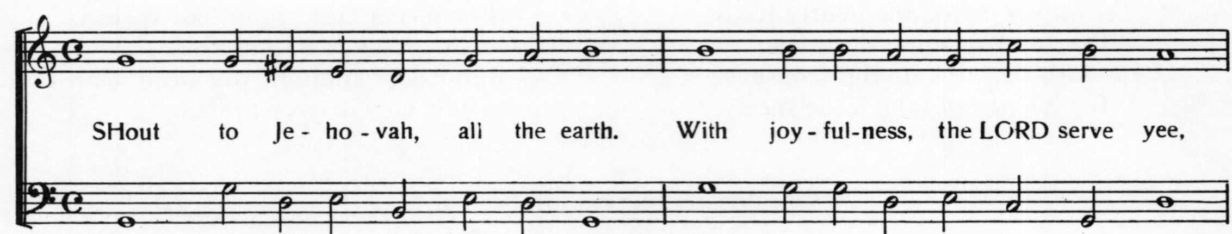

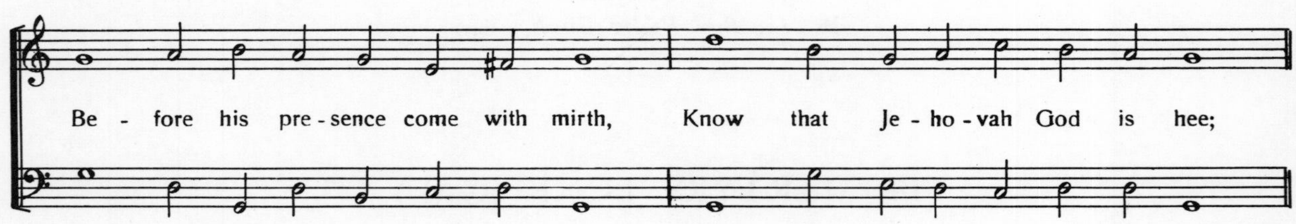

2

It's he that made us and not we,
His folk his pastures sheep also.
Into his gates with thanks come ye
With praises to his Court-yards go.

3

Give thanks to him, bless ye his Name
Because Jehovah he is good:
His mercy ever is the same:
His truth throughout all ages stood.

Ps. 100: *Bay Psalm Book*, 1698

16. PSALM 119 (C.M.D.)

1558

Bay Psalm Book
(Boston, 1698)

Ps. 119: *Bay Psalm Book*, 1698

17. PSALM 148 (H.M.)

Hallelujah

1558

Bay Psalm Book
(Boston, 1698)

2

Yee heav'ns of heav'ns him prayse.
'Bove heav'ns yee waters clear,
The LORDs Name let them prayse.
For he spake made they were
 Them stablisht hee
For ever and ay:
Nor pass away
 Shall his decree.

Ps. 148: *Bay Psalm Book*, 1698

18. ST. ANNE'S TUNE (C.M.)

1708

A Supplement to the New Version
Tate and Brady
(*London, 1708*)

William Croft
(1678–1727)

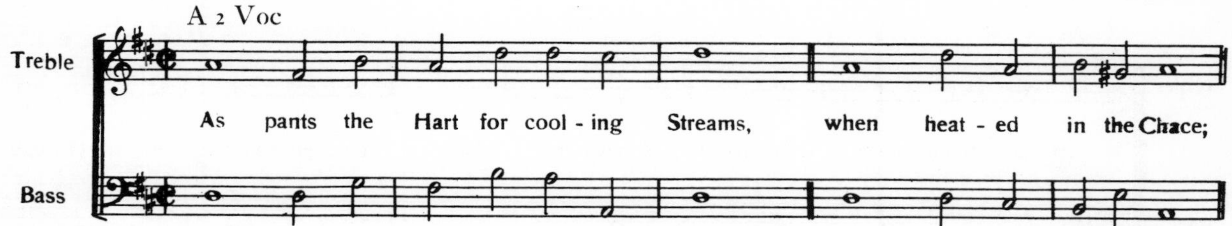

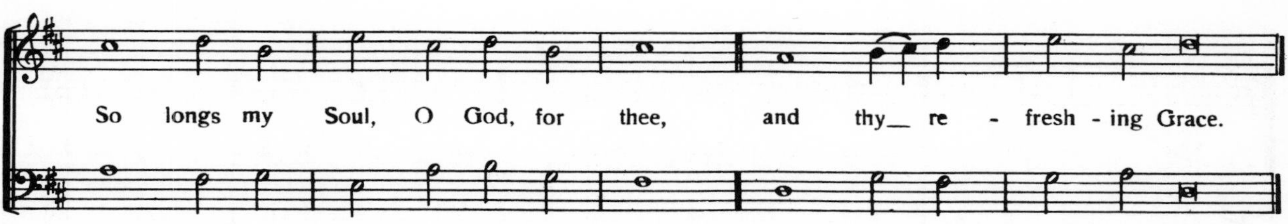

2

For thee, my God, the living God,
  my thirsty Soul doth pine;
O when shall I behold thy Face,
  thou Majesty Divine!

3

Tears are my constant Food, while thus
  insulting Foes upbraid,
"Deluded Wretch, where's now thy God?
  and where his promis'd Aid?"

Ps. 42: Nahum Tate (1698)
(1652–1715)

19. SONG OF THE ANGELS (C.M.)

(Winchester Tune)

1700

A Supplement to the New Version
Tate and Brady
(London, 1708)

2
"Fear not, said he, (for mighty Dread
"had seiz'd their troubled Mind);
"Glad Tidings of great Joy I bring
"to you, and all Mankind:

3
"To you, in David's Town, this Day
"is born, of David's Line,
"The Saviour, who is Christ the Lord;
"and This shall be the Sign:

4
"The heav'nly Babe you there shall find
"to humane View display'd,
"All meanly wrapt in swathing Bands,
"and in a Manger laid.

5
Thus spake the Seraph, and forthwith
appear'd a shining Throng
Of Angels praising God, and thus
address'd their joyful Song:

6
"All Glory be to God on high,
"and to the Earth be Peace:
"Good Will, henceforth, from Heav'n to Men,
"begin and never cease.

Luke 2: Nahum Tate (1700)
(1652–1715)

20. MEAR (C.M.)

1720

From a tune supplement for the *New Version*
Engraved, printed, and sold by Thomas Johnston
(*Boston, 1755*)

2
The mangled Bodies of thy Saints
abroad unburied lay;
Their Flesh expos'd to Savage Beasts,
and rav'nous Birds of Prey.

3
Quite thro' *Jerusalem* was their Blood
like common Water shed;
And none were left alive to pay
last Duties to the Dead.

Ps. 79: Nahum Tate (1698)
(1652–1715)

20a. MIDDLESEX (C.M.)

[*Mear*]

1720

A Sett of Tunes in 3 Parts
Simon Browne
(*London, 1720*)

Simon Browne?

[1] The A is a whole note, and the G is a half note in the original.

Hymns and Spiritual Songs, Simon Browne, 1720

Chapter Two

THE FIRST INSTRUCTION BOOKS AND SINGING SCHOOLS

1721-1764

Just Publish'd, & to be Sold by Samuel Gerrish, A Small Singing Book of 18 Psalm Tunes (both Trible and Bass) in the easy Method of Singing by Letters instead of Notes, first contrived by the Reverend Mr. TUFTS. Neatly engraven on Copper, with suitable directions, very Useful for People even of the meanest capacities, and for Children. Price 1s.

Boston News-Letter, January 21/28, 1723

THE SINGING of hymns and psalms in New England churches gradually deteriorated until at the beginning of the 18th century many congregations were unable to sing more than a few tunes and no two sang them alike. The dearth of printed music in America, and the lack of any means of music education, afforded little if any opportunity for learning to read music. Music was learned by rote, without the help of professional musicians, by a people who were for the most part musically illiterate. The practice of "lining-out" the psalm-tunes had gradually changed the lively singing of the early Puritans into a slow and often highly embellished type of psalm-singing, later called the "Common" or "Usual Way" of singing.

As the need for reform became increasingly apparent, leading ministers, among whom were the Rev. Thomas Symmes of Bradford, Massachusetts, the Rev. John Tufts of Newburyport, and the Rev. Thomas Walter of Roxbury (all contemporaries of J. S. Bach), took steps to improve the situation. Symmes wrote pamphlets and preached sermons on "The Reasonableness of Regular Singing or Singing by Note" (1720) and urged the people to return to the ways of the early New England settlers who could sing correctly by note, and to give up the "many turnings and flourishings with the voice." It remained for the Rev. John Tufts and the Rev. Thomas Walter to publish the first instruction books with music and to lay the foundation for music education in the United States.

The new "Correct" or "Regular Way" of singing by note was not immediately acceptable to all congregations, and many arguments ensued between the older conservatives who preferred the old "Common" or "Usual Way" and the more progressive groups who favored the new "Correct" or "Regular Way." It was not long, however, before the pleasure of meeting together and learning to sing by note in the "Correct Way" led to the establishment of the singing school. The need for music books eventually resulted in a flow of instruction books with music, and in the last decades of the 18th century the singing school became the principal source of music pedagogy, an important part of the social life, and a stimulus to native composers which lasted throughout the 19th century.

John Tufts's *An Introduction to the Singing of Psalm-Tunes*

The complete title page of the Rev. John Tufts's instruction book reads:

AN INTRODUCTION To the Singing OF *Psalm-Tunes,* In a plain & easy Method. With A COLLECTION of Tunes In Three Parts. By the Rev. Mr. TUFTS. The FIFTH EDITION. Printed from *Copper-Plates,* Neatly Engraven. BOSTON, in N.E. Printed for *Samuel Gerrish,* at the Lower End of Cornhill. 1726.

No copies of the first edition of 1721 (which contained twenty tunes in one part) nor of the subsequent three editions are known to exist. The first known edition, the fifth, was published in 1726 with 37 tunes set in three parts. Irving Lowens [1] has pointed out that 31 of Tufts's tunes are found in John Playford's *Whole Book of Psalms* (London, 1677) or in Thomas Walter's *Grounds and Rules of Musick Explained* (Boston, 1721), and that 21 of these tunes are found in all three collections.

In search of a system that would enable "People even of the meanest capacities and Children" to sing a tune at sight, Tufts used a letter notation that was well known in England and had already appeared underneath the notes in the *Bay Psalm Book* of 1698. Tufts, however, placed the letters F[a], S[ol], L[a], and M[i] on the staff in lieu of the notes. In his "Short Introduction To the Singing of PSALM-TUNES," he explains the notation, clefs, intervals, scales, keys, and time signatures. Tunes in triple time, he states, "are sung about One Third swifter than Common Time." Significantly, he mentions that the ability to sing intervals correctly is "not to be attained ordinarily, without the help of some skilful Person, or of an Instrument." The use of the cello ("the Lord's fiddle") and pitch-pipe in singing schools eventually led to their use in church.

Three tunes from Tufts's *Introduction* are included in the *Anthology*. The tune *Northampton* is one of three that Tufts evidently took from Simon Browne's *A Sett of Tunes in 3 Parts* (London, 1720). It had also appeared earlier in John Bishop's *A Set of New Psalm Tunes in Four Parts*, advertised in London in 1710. *Northampton* (No. 21) is unusual in being moderately florid, while almost all other

[1] Irving Lowens, "John Tufts' *Introduction to the Singing of Psalm-Tunes* (1721–1744): The First American Music Textbook," *Journal of Research in Music Education,* II (1954), 89–102.

previous settings of psalm-tunes are syllabic.

Tufts's acquaintance with Tate and Brady's *A Supplement to the New Version* (London, 1708) is apparent by his inclusion of *149 Psalm Tune* (No. 22), which first appeared anonymously in that collection. The strong melody, known since 1730 as *Hanover*, is attributed to William Croft and is included in a three-part setting for the first time in Tufts's *Introduction*. It is quite possible that Tufts himself supplied the Medius part.

The *100 Psalm Tune New* (No. 23) is perhaps the most interesting tune in Tufts's publication, not because of any esthetic considerations but because it may possibly be the first complete composition by a native American composer.[2] In the natural minor (Aeolian) mode, the piece is a rare example of a setting of *Psalm 100* in triple time.

Thomas Walter's *The Grounds and Rules of Musick Explained*

The subtitle of this instruction book with music, published in Boston in 1721, reads:

An *Introduction* to the Art of Singing by *Note*. Fitted to the meanest Capacities.

The "Recommendatory Preface" to the Rev. Thomas Walter's book was signed by fifteen ministers, including Walter's grandfather, Increase Mather (1639–1723), and his uncle, Cotton Mather (1663–1728). In the preamble to the *Grounds and Rules* Walter gives a clear picture of the sad state of music as he saw it. It reads in part:

[Once the tunes] were sung according to the Rules of the *Scale of Musick*, but are now miserably tortured, and twisted, and quavered, [ornamented] in some Churches, into a horrid Medly of confused and disorderly Noises . . . and there are no two Churches that sing alike. Yea, I have my self heard (for Instance) *Oxford* Tune sung in *three* Churches (which I purposely forbear to mention) with as much Difference as there can possibly be between *York* and *Oxford* or any two other different Tunes. . . . I have observed in many Places one Man is upon this Note, while another is a Note before him, which produces something so hideous and disorderly, as is beyond Expression bad.

Walter also complains about the "tedious Protraction of the Notes beyond the Compass of a Man's Breath" and says, "I my self have twice in one Note paused to take Breath." In regard to the "Old Way" of singing, Walter affirms that "the Notes sung according to the *Scale and Rules of Musick* are the true "*Old Way*," that is, the way of the early New England settlers.

The 24 tunes in Walter's *Grounds and Rules* were set in three parts without a text, and neatly engraved with regular bar-lines (for the first time in the Colonies). They include all thirteen tunes in the *Bay Psalm Book* of 1698, and 23 of Walter's tunes are also found in Tufts's *Introduction* (1726). Playford's *Whole Book of Psalms . . . Composed in Three Parts* (1677) was the principal source for Walter's settings. The Introduction to his *Grounds and Rules*, although lacking the conciseness and clarity of Tufts's, includes "Some brief and very plain Instructions for Singing by Note."

London Tune (No. 24, not to be confused with *London New*) was named *Litchfield* by Playford (1671), and his two-part setting of the tune called *Lichfield* [*sic*] is one of the thirteen in the *Bay Psalm Book* (1698). The hexatonic melody, with the seventh omitted, is of special interest, for it begins in dominant harmony; either by accident or design Walter has changed Playford's original version by lowering the sixth degree of the scale.

The tune *Southwel New* (No. 25) has not been located in earlier sources and may have been composed entirely by Walter. If so, it

[2] *Ibid.*, pp. 97–99.

would antedate Tufts's *100 Psalm Tune New* by several years and would be the first composition by a native-born American.

The rhythmic pattern of the familiar *100 Psalm Tune* (No. 26), typical of Playford's settings, is found in the *Bay Psalm Book* (1698) but varies from the patterns of most earlier versions. This is the first three-part setting of the *100 Psalm Tune* to be published in America.

The Collections of William Tans'ur and Aaron Williams

One of the strong influences on the composers of early sacred music in America was the popular *The Royal Melody Compleat: or, The New Harmony of Sion* (London, 1755) by William Tans'ur (Tanzer), an English composer-compiler and theoretician. His "new and correct introduction to the grounds of musick" in *The Royal Melody* was extensively copied by William Billings and other early New England composers. Daniel Bayley (c. 1725–1799) published the first American edition of *The Royal Melody* in Boston in 1767, and by 1774 the work had gone through seven editions.[3]

Selections of music from the *Universal Psalmodist* (London, 1763) by another English psalmodist, Aaron Williams, were included in Bayley's early editions of *The Royal Melody*. In 1769, Bailey [*sic*] brought out the fifth edition with a new title, *The American Harmony: or, Royal Melody Complete* and incorporated Williams's *Universal Psalmodist* as the second part of the book.

Following the trend toward a livelier type of church music, partly the result of the evangelical revival in England, Tans'ur added "fuging" choruses to some of his psalm-tunes, suggesting, however, that they "may be omitted, where *Voices* can't be had to perform them according to *Art*."

Tans'ur's *Westerham* (No. 27) is an 18th-century example of an added fuging chorus, a form of imitative writing that had been in use in England since the late 16th century. This type of English psalmody was also well known in New England and was imitated by Billings in his comparatively few fuging tunes.

St. Martin's tune by Tans'ur (No. 28), with Tate and Brady's version of *Psalm 78*, is still sung today by the alumni at Harvard commencements.

Aaron Williams's *St. Thomas's* (No. 29) is another tune that has stood the test of time, and except for the melody being in the soprano it is found in modern hymnals in almost the identical form of the original.

Josiah Flagg's *A Collection of the Best Psalm Tunes*

Josiah Flagg took an active part in the concert life of Boston and introduced many foreign musicians there, among them William Selby. His collection of psalm-tunes, engraved on copper plates by Paul Revere, included 116 psalm-tunes in two, three, and four parts and two anthems ("the greater part of them never before printed in America") and was published in Boston in 1764. *Hallelujah* (No. 30), taken from Flagg's collection, is an interesting example of five-part writing and the use of imitation, the trumpet-like theme even ap-

[3] A bibliographical study of Daniel Bayley's *The American Harmony* by Irving Lowens and Allen P. Britton appeared in the *Papers* of the Bibliographical Society of America, Vol. 49, Fourth Quarter, 1955.

pearing in stretto and augmentation. Flagg published a second collection in 1766 which contained upwards of twenty anthems by English composers. The anthems in his two collections and Daniel Bayley's edition of Tans'ur's *Royal Melody* (1767) served as models for American composers, particularly in New England.[4]

[4] Ralph T. Daniel, "English Models for the First American Anthems," *Journal of the American Musicological Society*, XII (1959), 49–58.

21. NORTHAMPTON (C.M.)

c. 1710

An Introduction to the Singing of Psalm-Tunes
John Tufts
(*Boston, 1726*)

[1] This note is A in Tufts's *Introduction* and in Browne's *Sett of Tunes*, 1720. Bishop (c. 1710) has G.

2

But he upon Jehovah's law
doth set his whole delight,
And in his law doth meditate
both in the day and night.

3

He shall be like a planted tree
by water-brooks which shall
In his due season use his fruit,
whose leaf shall never fail.

4

And all he doth, shall prosper well,
the wicked are not so:
But they are like unto the chaff
which wind drives to and fro.

5

For of the righteous men, the Lord
acknowledgeth the way:
Where as the way of wicked men
shall utterly decay.

Ps. 1: *Bay (New England) Psalm Book*, 1651

22. 149 PSALM TUNE (10.10.11.11.)

(*Hanover*)

1708

An Introduction to the Singing of Psalm-Tunes
John Tufts
(*Boston, 1726*)

William Croft
(1678–1727)

[1] F in the original.
[2] B-flat in the original.
[3] E-flat in the original.

2

Let them his great Name extol in the Dance;
With Timbrel and Harp his praises express;
Who always takes pleasure his Saints to ad-
vance,
And with his Salvation the Humble to bless.
Ps. 149: *New Version*, Tate and Brady, 1698

23. 100 PSALM TUNE NEW (L.M.)

1726

An Introduction to the Singing of Psalm-Tunes
John Tufts
(*Boston, 1726*)

John Tufts?
(1689–1750)

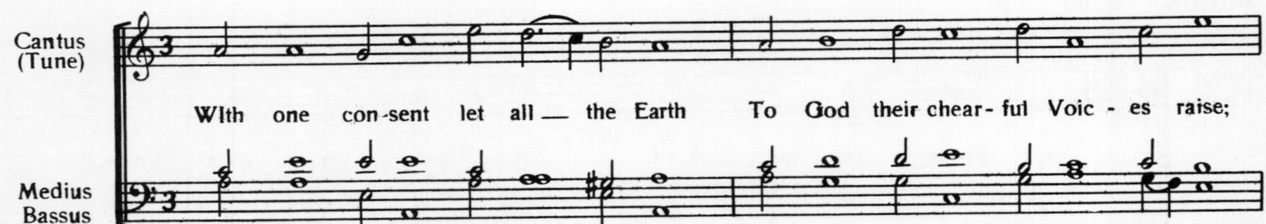

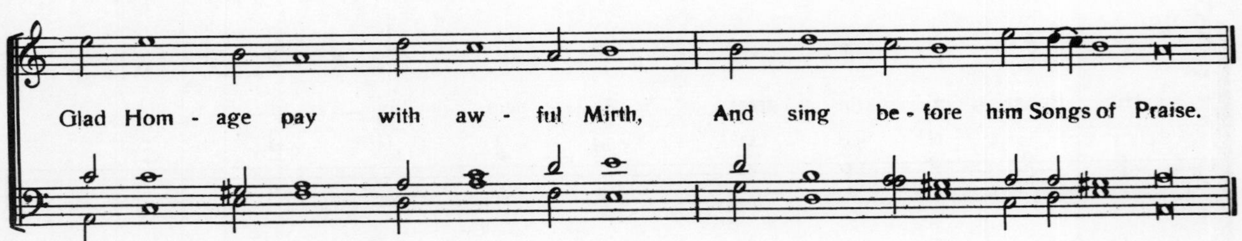

2
Convinc'd that he is God alone,
From whom both we and all proceed;
We, whom he chuses for his own,
The Flock that he vouchsafes to feed.

3
O enter then his Temple-Gate
Thence to his Courts devoutly press,
And still your grateful Hymns repeat,
And still his Name with Praises bless.

Ps. 100: *New Version*, Tate and Brady, 1698

24. LONDON TUNE (C.M.)

(*Litchfield*)

1677

The Grounds and Rules of Musick Explained
Thomas Walter
(*Boston, 1721*)

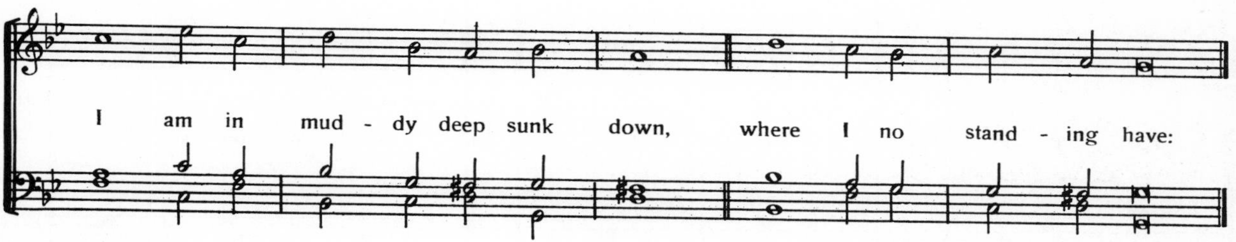

2
Into deep waters I am come,
  where floods me overflow.
I of my crying weary am;
  my throat is dried so.

3
Mine eyes fail, for my God I wayt.
  They that have hated mee
Without a cause, then mine heads hairs,
  they more in number bee:

4
Also mine enemies wrongfully
  they are that would me slay,
They mighty are, then I restor'd
  what I took not away.

5
O God thou know'st my foolishness,
  my sin's not hid from thee.
Who wayt on thee, Lord GOD of hoasts,
  let not be sham'd for mee:

Ps. 69: *Bay (New England) Psalm Book*, 1651

25. SOUTHWEL NEW (S.M.)

1721

The Grounds and Rules of Musick Explained
Thomas Walter
(*Boston, 1721*)

Thomas Walter?
(1696–1725)

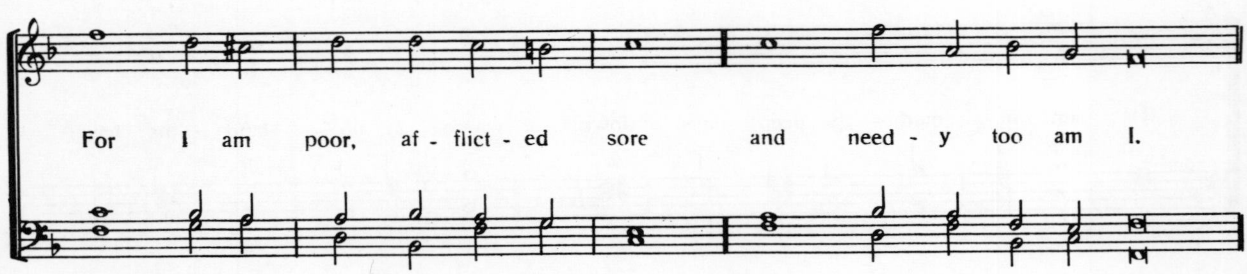

[1] This note is G in the original.

2

In safety keep my soul,
 for gracious am I.
My God save thou thy servant now,
 that doth on thee rely.

3

Jehovah gracious
 O be thou unto mee:
Because that I aloud do cry
 Through all the day to thee.

4

O make thy servants soul
 that it may joyfull bee:
Because that I O LORD, on high
 do lift my soul to thee.

5

For thou O LORD art good,
 to pardon prone also;
And to them all on thee that call
 in mercy rich art thou.

Ps. 86: *Bay* (*New England*) *Psalm Book*, 1651

26. 100 PSALM TUNE (L.M.)

1677

The Grounds and Rules of Musick Explained
Thomas Walter
(*Boston, 1721*)

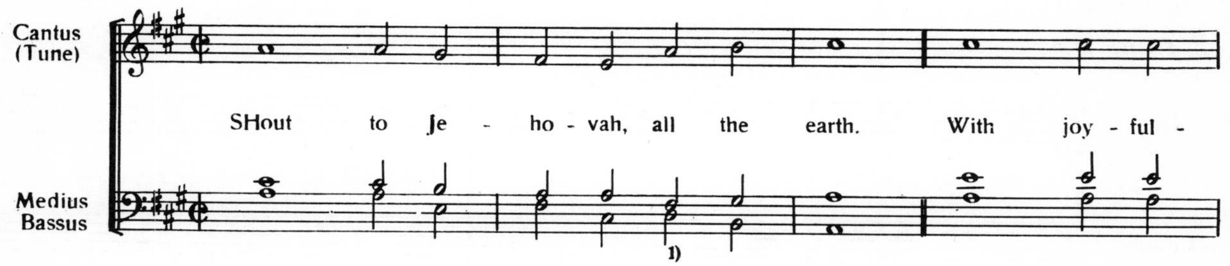

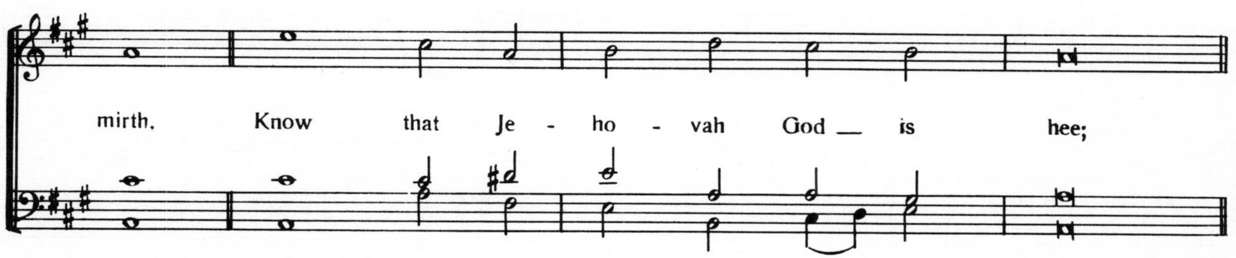

[1] B-flat in the original.

2

It's he that made us, and not wee,
His folk, his pasture sheep also.
Into his gates with thanks come yee:
With prayses to his Court-yards go.

3

Give thanks to him, bless ye his name,
Because Jehovah he is good:
His mercy ever is the same,
His trueth throughout all ages stood.

Ps. 100: *Bay (New England) Psalm Book*, 1651

27. WESTERHAM TUNE (C.M.)

Psalm 81

1755

The Royal Melody Complete: or, The New Harmony of Zion
William Tans'ur, Sr.
(*Boston, 1767*)

William Tans'ur, Sr.
(1706–1783)

Lift up your Voice, To Ja - cob's God al - way.
and lift up your Voice, To Ja - cob's God al - way.
and lift up your Voice, To Ja - cob's God al - way.
Lift up your Voice, To Ja - cob's God al - way.
Chorus
Be
Be joy - - full. and lift
Be joy - - full, and be joy - - full, and lift

Be joy - full, and lift up your Voice, To
joy - full, and be joy - full, and lift up your Voice, To
up your Voice, be joy - full, and lift up your Voice, To
up your Voice, be joy - full, and lift up your Voice, To
Ja - - - - cob's God al - way.
Ja - - - - cob's God al - way.
Ja - - - - cob's God al - way.
Ja - - - - cob's God al - way.

28. ST. MARTIN'S (C.M.)

1755

The American Harmony: or, Royal Melody Complete
William Tans'ur, Sr.
(*Newbury-Port, 1769*)

William Tans'ur, Sr.
(1706–1783)

Ps. 78: *New Version*, Tate and Brady, 1717

29. ST. THOMAS'S (S.M.)

1770

The Universal Psalmodist
Aaron Williams
(*London, 1770*)

Aaron Williams
(1731–1776)

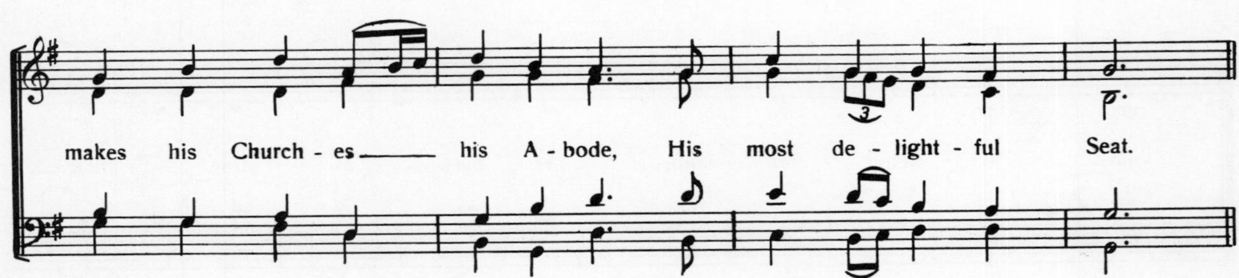

2

These Temples of his Grace,
How beautifull they Stand,
The Honours of our Native place,
And Bulwarks of our Land.

Ps. 48: Isaac Watts (1719)
(1674–1748)

30. HALLELUJAH

A Chorus for 5 Voices

1764

A Collection of the Best Psalm-Tunes
Josiah Flagg
(*Boston, 1764*)

Josiah Flagg?
(1738–1794)

Hal - le - lu - jah, Hal-le-lu - jah, Hal-le - - lu -
Hal-le-lu-jah, Hal-le-lu-jah, Hal-le-lu - jah, Hal-le - lu - -
-lu - jah, Hal-le-lu-jah, Hal - le - lu - jah, Hal - le -
Hal - le - lu - jah, Hal-le-lu-jah,
Hal-le-lu-jah, Hal - le - lu - jah, Hal - le - lu - -

jah.
jah, Hal - le - lu - - jah.
lu - jah, Hal - le - lu - - jah.
Hal-le-lu-jah, Hal-le-lu-jah, Hal - le - lu - - jah.
jah, Hal - le - lu - - jah.

Chapter Three

THE MUSIC OF THE EPHRATA CLOISTER AND THE MORAVIANS

"While at Bethlehem, I inquir'd a little into the practice of the Moravians: some of them had accompanied me, and all were very kind to me. . . . I was at their church, where I was entertain'd with good musick, the organ being accompanied with violins, hautboys, flutes, clarinets, etc."

The Autobiography of Benjamin Franklin

The Ephrata Cloister

FOR THE first hundred years the mainstream of musical activity in America centered in New England. Early in the 18th century, however, a strong musical current was felt in Philadelphia, Charleston, and New York. Pennsylvania, a Quaker province, became a refuge for many religious sects from Central Europe, particularly from Germany. One of these groups, a semi-monastic community of Seventh-Day Baptists, was established in 1732 by Conrad Beissel at Ephrata ("the beautiful") in Lancaster County.[1]

[1] Hans David has made a comparison of Ephrata and Bethlehem in Pennsylvania, published in the *Papers of the American Musicological Society*, 1941.

Music played an important part in the religious services at the Ephrata Cloister, and Beissel organized and trained a chorus capable of singing in as many as eight parts, with antiphonal singing an important feature. Music of European composers was not drawn on, however, and in addition to managing all the affairs of the Cloister the indefatigable Beissel composed over a thousand hymns and even settings of whole chapters from the Old Testament. Instrumental accompaniments were not indicated, but the lower part was often played by an instrument, with instruments possibly doubling the other voices.

Virtually a self-taught composer, Beissel

developed his own unorthodox and highly original theories of composition, which are demonstrated in his setting of the text, *Gott ein Herrscher aller Heyden* (No. 31). Chords in root position are interchanged indiscriminately with second inversions, and hymns may even begin with a second inversion. Parallel fifths and octaves are a common occurrence. There is little if any use of modulation or suspensions, and dissonances appear only as passing notes. An occasional brief imitation between two parts is as far as Beissel was able to go in counterpoint. The music was sung rather freely, the rhythm following the text. Stressed syllables were held longer, the length depending on the amount of stress the syllable received.

The activities of the Ephrata Cloister were known to many Pennsylvania families whose children attended their schools and to such leaders as Francis Hopkinson, George Washington, and Benjamin Franklin (who printed one of the Ephrata hymnals as early as 1730). However, the music composed by Beissel and his successor, Peter Miller, although interesting as an example of primitive art, lacked the ingredients necessary for it to have any lasting significance.

Music of the Moravians

In 1732 a small band of members of the *Unitas Fratrem* (Unity of Brethren), spiritual descendants of the Bohemian reformer, John Hus, sought refuge in Georgia; they later moved to Nazareth, Pennsylvania, and in 1741 founded Bethlehem. The missionary zeal of the Moravians, as they came to be known, also led to the establishment of other communities, notably in Lititz, Pennsylvania, and Salem, North Carolina.

The activities at the communities were numerous and varied, especially at Bethlehem, where an intensively active musical life developed. A *Collegium musicum* was formed in 1744 and performed throughout the years choral, chamber, and symphonic works by Karl F. Abel, Johann Christoph Friedrich Bach, Johann Stamitz, Handel, Graun, Haydn, Mozart, and many other composers, often for the first time in America.

Trombone choirs were organized; they have remained an integral part of Moravian life up to the present time. The concerts by the *Collegium musicum* attracted music lovers from Philadelphia and New York as well as other communities. The work of the Moravians became known to many prominent men, including the Marquis de Lafayette, George Washington, and Benjamin Franklin.

In 1766 a Moravian composer, Jeremiah Dencke, wrote the first sacred music in America with an instrumental accompaniment. Other professionally trained Moravian musicians, who modelled their style after the pre-Classical Central Europeans, composed the first chamber music in America and wrote elaborate arias and choruses with instrumental accompaniment for use in church. The art of organ building was developed, especially by David Tannenberg (1728–1804) of Lititz, who constructed organs along the lines of those by the famous German builders Arp Schnitger (1648–1720) and Gottfried Silbermann (1683–1753). Woodwinds, strings, and brasses were imported, since comparatively few of these instruments were made here until the early 19th century.

The period of the Moravians' greatest musical activity and accomplishment began about 1770, the date of William Billings's first publication, *The New-England Psalm-Singer*. By 1850 the Moravian force was spent, but the musical tradition was handed down by Johann C. Till (1762–1844) and Peter Wolle (1792–1871), both pupils of Johann Friedrich Peter (1746–1813). Today Bethlehem is known by the annual performances of the Bach Choir, and music by the Moravians is heard in church and concert with increasing frequency.

Three outstanding Moravian composers, John Antes, Johann Friedrich Peter, and David Moritz Michael, are represented in the *Anthology*. The music was chosen by Dr. Donald M. McCorkle,[2] Director of The Moravian Music Foundation, and represents a cross section of the finest Moravian compositions.

John Antes's preferred medium was the anthem, 25 of which have been found. Some are solo anthems, while others call for a four-part chorus, but in all cases they are supplied with an instrumental accompaniment, usually strings and only rarely with the addition of two horns and continuo. According to Dr. McCorkle, *Go, congregation, go!* (No. 32) and *Surely He has borne our griefs* (No. 33) were intended to be performed as a unit, the resulting form being what the English often loosely termed an Ode. These two outstanding compositions were originally scored for strings, and their poignancy and melodic beauty point to Antes as one of the most able American-born composers of his time.

The first chamber works by a native-born American composer were three trios for two violins and cello, also by John Antes. They were composed, probably between 1779–1781, while he was a missionary in Cairo, and were published in London. At a time when compositions for small string groups often focused the melodic interest on the first violin, Antes expertly distributed the melody and accompaniment figures among all three instruments. The influence of Haydn is apparent in these works, and there is some evidence that he knew Haydn and his string trios. The first movement, Allegro, of the Trio II in D minor, Opus 3, is in the conventional sonata-allegro form (No. 34). The other two movements of the Trio are Andante un poco Adagio and Presto.

Johann Friedrich (John Frederik) Peter, who went to Salem in 1780, composed six quintets for two violins, two violas, and one cello, which have survived in a holograph score and parts dated January 9, 1789. The thoroughness of his study of the music of pre-Classical European composers, as well as Haydn, is reflected in the form and the harmonic and melodic styles of the quintets. The second movement (Adagio) of Quintet V (No. 35) is in binary form, and it reveals Peter's progressive harmonic style and freedom of modulation. The two violins and two violas are handled in pairs, while the cello, assigned to its principal function as bass, occasionally joins the violin or viola in short passages in thirds or sixths.

I will make an everlasting covenant (No. 36), originally scored for strings, is one of Peter's finest sacred songs. He achieves unity in this through-composed solo through repetitions of the 16th-note motif, the frequent use of appoggiaturas at the ends of phrases, and the simple rhythmic pattern of the voice part. Of special interest are the uneven lengths of the phrases.

Although David Moritz Michael composed anthems and sacred ariettas, his most unusual contributions were fourteen *Parthien*, or Suites, for two clarinets, two horns, one or two bassoons, and an additional flute or trumpet. It is not fanciful to imagine these compositions as works intended for "al fresco" performances, for two of these wind sextets were actually composed as "water music" and were played on a barge excursion on the Lehigh River. In the first movement of *Parthia No. 1*, which is in binary form, Michael demonstrates a thorough knowledge of wind instruments (No. 37).

Dr. McCorkle[3] has pointed out that very little of the music of the Moravians became a part of musical life in America. The Moravians did, however, contribute to the musical culture through their instruments, their *Collegia musica*, their first performances of major European oratorios and symphonies, and the quantity and quality of their various musical activities.

[2] Dr. McCorkle's many articles on Moravian music and musicians are available from The Moravian Music Foundation, Winston-Salem, North Carolina.

[3] Donald M. McCorkle, "The Moravian Contribution to American Music," Music Library Association *Notes*, XIII (Dec. 1956).

31. GOTT EIN HERRSCHER ALLER HEYDEN

1747

Turtel-Taube
(Ephrata, 1747)

Johann Conrad Beissel
(1690–1768)

und ihr recht las - sen hoch her-gehn an sei - nem Ei - gen-thum, dass nun giebt Preiss und Ruhm.
so wird man Freud und Won - ne sehen
und ihr recht las - sen hoch her-gehn an sei - nem Ei - gen-thum, dass nun giebt Preiss und Ruhm.
so wird man Freud und Won - ne sehen
und ihr recht las - sen hoch her-gehn an sei - nem Ei - gen-thum, dass nun giebt Preiss und Ruhm.
so wird man Freud und Won - ne sehen

Gott — dem Kö - nig, der sie er- höht, ihr Völ - ker seht! wie — Got -tes Braut — nun ein- her - geht.
Gott — dem Kö - nig, der sie er- höht ihr Völ - ker seht! wie — Got -tes Braut — nun ein- her-geht.
Gott — dem Kö - nig, der sie er - höht, ihr Völ - ker seht! wie — Got - tes Braut — nun ein - her - geht.

32. GO, CONGREGATION, GO!

Aria for Soprano

c. 1795

Christian Gregor
(1723–1801)

John Antes
(1740–1811)
Edited and arranged by
Donald M. McCorkle

Note: *tr* indicates the points at which double trills (in the top voices simultaneously) are used in the original accompaniment. Since it is impossible to transcribe this device for keyboard, it may be more satisfactory to omit all such trills.

(9)
iour, thy Sav - iour in Geth - se - ma -
tr
ne;
rinf.
tr
(ten.)
B
(II)
(9)
Go, con - gre - ga - tion, go! go and
p
see, go and see thy Sav - iour, thy Sav - iour
(tr)

C
in Geth - se - ma - ne: There is a
tr
p
scene, a scene which with a maze must strike thee;
rinf.
(p)
rinf.
p
There, as - ton - - ished gaze, thy Mak er
(Mas ter)
rinf.
(pp)
rinf.
pp
prays, thy Mak - er prays.
(Mas - ter)

33. SURELY HE HAS BORNE OUR GRIEFS

Anthem for Mixed Voices

c. 1795

Isaiah 53: 4, 5

John Antes
(1740–1811)
Edited and arranged by
Donald M. McCorkle

griefs and car - - ried our sor - - rows.
griefs and car - - ried our sor - - rows.
griefs and car - - ried our sor - - rows.
griefs and car - - ried our sor - - rows.
A
He was wound - - ed for our trans -
He was wound - - ed for our trans -
He was wound - - ed for our trans -
He was wound - - ed for our trans -

gress - - ions, He was bruis - ed for
gress - - ions, He was bruis - ed for
gress - - ions, He was bruis - ed for
gress - - ions, He was bruis - ed for

our in - i - qui - ties;
our in - i - qui - ties;
our in - i - qui - ties;
our in - i - qui - ties;

B
The chas - tise - ment of our peace lay up -
The chas - tise - ment of our peace lay up -
8
The chas - tise - ment of our peace lay up -
The chas - tise - ment of our peace lay up -
on Him: And with His stripes we are heal -
on Him; And with His stripes we are heal -
8
on Him; And with His stripes we are heal -
on Him: And with His stripes we are heal -
tr

34. TRIO II

from

Tre Trii, per due Violini and Violoncello, Obligato

c. 1779/81

First Movement

John Antes
(1740–1811)
Edited and arranged by
Thor Johnson and Donald M. McCorkle

10
(dolce)

f
(f)
f
20

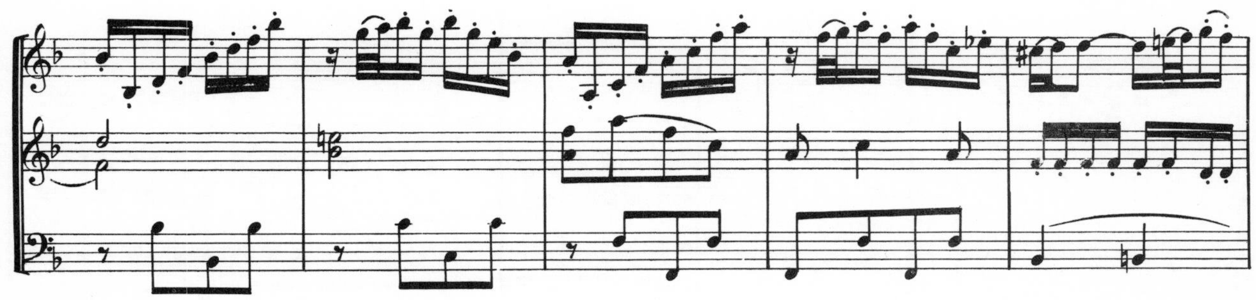

30
p
Solo
dolce
dolce
40
p
ff
p
ff
p
ff

50
Solo
dolce
f
60
rinf.
p
70

80
Solo
f
p
rinf.
(rinf.)
90
dolce
100

110
Solo
f
f
f
pp
pp tutti(a) una corda
p(p)
120
Solo
(dolce)
(dolce)
130
f
(f)
(f)
ff
ff
ff

140
p
p
p
rinf.
rinf.
rinf.
(Solo)
Solo
p
dolce
150
rinf.
rinf.
160
p
p
p
ff
ff
ff

35. QUINTET V

from

Six Quintetti a Due Violini, Due Viole, e Violoncello

1789

Second Movement

Johann Friedrich Peter
(1746–1813)
Edited by Hans T. David

tr
cresc.
f
p
pp
mf
f

ff
tr
mf
p
cresc.
f
pp

36. I WILL MAKE AN EVERLASTING COVENANT

Ich will mit euch einen ewigen Bund machen

1782

Isaiah 55: 3
(Original in German)

Johann Friedrich Peter
(1746–1813)
Edited and arranged by
Thor Johnson and Donald M. McCorkle

Original in D major.
Note: *tr* indicates the points at which double trills (in the top voices simultaneously) are used in the original accompaniment. Since it is impossible to transcribe this device for keyboard, it will be more satisfactory to omit all such trills.

(p)
an ev - er - last - ing
Ich will mit euch, mit
p
cov - e - nant, I will make, I will make, will
euch ei - nen e - - wi - gen Bund, ei - nen e - wi - gen
make with you,
Bund ma - chen,
f
(p)
an
Ich
p
ev - er - last - ing cov - e - nant with you, I will make with
will mit euch, mit euch ei - nen e - wi - gen Bund, ei - nen e - wi - gen

(pp)
you an ev - er - last - - - ing cov - - e - nant,
Bund, ei - nen e - - wi - gen Bund ma - chen,
pp
mf
f
(mf)
e - ven, e - ven the sure mer - cies of
näm - lich, die ge - wis - sen Gna - den
mf
Da - vid, the sure mer - - cies of Da - - -
Da - vids, die ge - wis - sen Gna - den Da - - -
(cresc.)
vid.
vids.
f
(poco rit.)

37. PARTHIA NO. 1

First Movement

c. 1807

David Moritz Michael
(1751–1827)
Edited by Donald M. McCorkle

Cl.
Trpt.
Hn.
Bsn.
B
Cl.
Trpt.
Hn.
Bsn.

C
Cl.
Trpt.
Hn.
Bsn.
Cl.
Trpt.
Hn.
Bsn.

D
Cl.
Trpt.
Hn.
Bsn.
f
p
Cl.
Trpt.
Hn.
Bsn.

E
Cl.
Trpt.
Hn.
Bsn.
(p)
f
p
(f)

F
Cl.
Trpt.
Hn.
Bsn.
f
p
(f)
(p)
Cl.
Trpt.
Hn.
Bsn.

G
Cl.
Trpt.
Hn.
Bsn.
Cl.
Trpt.
Hn.
Bsn.

H
Cl.
Trpt.
Hn.
Bsn.
f
p
(f)

J
Cl.
Trpt.
Hn.
Bsn.
K
Cl.
Trpt.
Hn.
Bsn.

Cl.

Trpt.

Hn.

Bsn.

p f (p) p f p (f) (p) (f) (p) (f) (p) (f) (p)

L

Cl.

Trpt.

Hn.

Bsn.

(p) (f) (p) (f) (p) (f) (p) (f) (p) (f) (p) (f)

Chapter Four

NATIVE AMERICAN COMPOSERS

1759-1810

Enlisted in the cause of sin,
Why should a good be evil?
Music, alas, too long has been
Press'd to obey the devil.
Jeremiah Ingalls

Known as our first native American composers, Francis Hopkinson and James Lyon stand apart from the sturdy, self-made New England composers of the last three decades of the 18th century.

Hopkinson, one of America's most versatile men, belonged to a circle of gentlemen amateurs who were active in the musical life of Philadelphia. He began to compose while still a student; and in 1759, at the age of twenty-two, he wrote his art-song, *My days have been so wondrous free* (No. 38), the first known composition by a native American composer.

Hopkinson's songs were modelled after those of popular contemporary English composers, among whom were Arne, Shield, and Storace. The songs were written in two parts, treble and bass, and the harpsichordist was expected to fill in the harmonies according to his own discretion or ability. Although not without charm, the lack of originality and limited circulation prevented the songs from having any real influence on the development of music in America.

George Washington, emerging as the military and political leader of our new nation, became the subject for many songs, among them *A Toast* written by his friend, Francis Hopkinson (No. 39). The music is stylistically akin to the English national anthem, and several measures were apparently freely borrowed.

The Rev. James Lyon published in Philadelphia, 1761, a collection with the following title:

Urania, or a Choice Collection of Psalm-Tunes, Anthems, and Hymns, From the most approved Authors, with some Entirely New, in Two, Three and Four Parts. The whole Peculiarly adapted to the Use of CHURCHES and PRIVATE FAMILIES. To which are Prefixed The Plainest & most Necessary Rules of Psalmody.

The music was entirely by English composers except for six original compositions by Lyon. The tune *God Save the King* appeared for the first time in America in Lyon's *Urania*, where it was called *Whitefield's* (No. 40) and set to the hymn *Come Thou Almighty King*, taken from the hymn collection of the great English Methodist revivalist, George Whitefield (1714–1770).

Lyon's *Friendship* (No. 41), one of his most important compositions, was first published anonymously in 1774 in John Stickney's extensive collection *Gentleman and Lady's Musical Companion*. The somewhat florid anthem or ode is in three sections, all integrated through the use of a group of 16th notes which appears in the various voices at different times. The effective middle section, in the tonic minor key of G, reflects the sentiment of the text, "in floods our sorrows roll."

By 1770 the singing school, which had its beginnings in New England in the first decades of the 18th century, had developed into a flourishing institution. The demand for music and instruction was met by a talented group of self-taught composer-compilers who published over 370 tunebooks before 1811.

The typical New England musician of the period 1770–1810 was a hardy and enthusiastic individual steeped in the heritage of psalm-singing, a man of modest circumstances and humble occupation. He was a composer, a compiler of tunebooks, and a singing master who traveled through the countryside holding classes in taverns, schools, and churches. Most of these men had a limited education, a few were college graduates. Some were prominent in politics and became leading citizens; others fought in the Revolution.

The music in the tunebooks included psalm-tunes, hymns, fuging tunes, anthems, and set pieces, and it was "designed for the use of singing-schools, musical societies, and churches." Thus, the same music served the secular as well as the religious needs of the people and was a part of their everyday life.

The theoretical part of the tunebooks varied from elementary explanations to extensive treatises covering music theory, tone production, and interpretative suggestions. A detailed explanation of the balance of voices in the chorus was often included. In general the bass was heavily emphasized. William Billings, whose lively introductions are of special interest, recommended that in a chorus of 40 voices, twenty should sing the bass, with the other twenty divided among the upper parts. He also preferred two or three voices on the parts marked "solo" and suggested that these be sung softly until all the parts join in the chorus as strong as possible.

Jacob Kimball (*Rural Harmony*, 1793) gives some suggestions for interpretation and states:

In a company of singers it would have a good effect for some of the performers on each part to be silent when passages marked *piano* occur; the additional strength of their voices in the *forte*, which generally precedes or succeeds the *piano* would mark the contrast more distinctly and give peculiar force and energy to the performance. In fuguing music, the strength of the voices should increase as the parts fall in.

With reference to double or "choosing" notes in one part, Kimball advised that the singers should divide the notes equally between them. Other writers suggested that one or the other note be chosen.

As for tone production, Simeon Jocelin (*Chorister's Companion*, 1782) wrote:

Let the voice be clear and smooth as possible neither forcing the sound through the nose, nor blowing through the teeth with the mouth shut. . . . a trembling of the voice is also carefully to be avoided. . . . the notes should not be struck abruptly like the report of a smith's hammer, but should be begun and ended soft, swelling greatly

> as the air of the tune requires. Notes of 2 beats admit of a double swell, the first fullest, the second soft like an echo. High notes should be sung soft, but not faint; low notes full but not harsh. Let the bass be sung bold and majestic, the tenor firm and manly, the counter clear and lofty, and the treble soft and delicate.

All vocal music of this period was written in open score, and the principal melody (air or tune) was invariably placed in the tenor voice in all part-music for four voices; only in the early 19th century did it find its way up to the treble voice. It was the usual practice for a few treble voices to sing the tenor part an octave higher than the men and for a few tenors to sing the treble part an octave lower than the women. Billings enthusiastically wrote that "a tune so sung (although it has but four parts) is in effect the same as six. Such a conjunction of masculine and feminine voices is beyond expression sweet and ravishing." The doubling of voices may not have been followed strictly, however, since it was customary to sing the tunes with any combination of singers that was available. The fuging sections were often sung without doubling the voices, some tunes were sung throughout in four-part harmony, and on occasion the sopranos and tenors may have exchanged parts. Another possibility is the doubling of the tenor by a few sopranos, but not the doubling of the sopranos by the tenors. Pitches were set by the singing master with a pitch-pipe and were probably lower than the present-day pitch.

The tempos were often indicated by the time signatures, and for this reason the latter have been retained in the *Anthology*. The piano reductions of the part-music have, however, been given conventional time signatures. It must be kept in mind that the deciding factor in the choice of a tempo should, of course, rest in the character of the text and the music. Jacob Kimball gave the following good advice: "A performer should endeavor to form a proper idea of the author's design in a piece of music, and his own judgment and taste must be his principal directors in doing justice to it." The table below summarizes the time signatures as given by Billings in his *Continental Harmony* (Boston, 1794), with their approximate metronomic equivalents.

C	Adagio	quarter note equals	60
C [¢]	Largo	quarter note equals	80
Ↄ̸ [Ↄ]	Allegro	half note equals	60
2/4		quarter note equals	120
6/4		dotted half note equals	80
6/8		dotted quarter note equals	80
3/2		half note equals	60
3/4		quarter note equals	80
3/8		dotted quarter note equals	53

Twenty-eight compositions by eighteen New England composers are included in this chapter of the *Anthology*. The composers were all born before 1780, and the music was published between 1770 and 1810.

At first the composers were strongly influenced by the English church music found in the collections of William Tans'ur, Aaron Williams, Josiah Flagg, and James Lyon. Towards the close of the Revolutionary War, however, a characteristically American music began to appear in the psalm-tunes and fuging tunes of Daniel Read, Simeon Jocelin, Lewis Edson, Timothy Swan, and many others. This new idiom, with its elements of folk music and harmonic vitality, spread rapidly and dominated the tunebooks until the early 19th century, when public taste began to demand imported European music.

The stylistic traits in this strong and highly original American music include folk-like tunes, irregular phrase-lengths, natural minor (Aeolian) and gapped scales, and virile rhythms. Unconventional harmonic progressions, parallel fifths and octaves, triadic and dyadic harmonies, occasional rhythmic independence of voices (fuging), sudden dissonances derived from contrapuntal part-writing, and the lack of suspensions are among some of the other important characteristics of this music.[1] The

[1] Allen P. Britton has summarized "The Musical Idiom in Early American Tunebooks" in an abstract

personality, environment, and musical independence of these composers are reflected in their music, and they composed, as Billings said, without being "confin'd to any Rules for Composition."

Among the basically homophonic compositions represented here are Billings's *Chester* (No. 43) and *Conquest* (No. 46), Swan's *China* (No. 53, named for a town in Maine), Belknap's *Summer* and *Autumn* (Nos. 63, 64), Holyoke's *Arnheim* (No. 66, written when he was sixteen),[2] and Read's *Windham* (No. 50). Billings's *Jargon* (No. 44), composed as a sarcastic answer to some of his critics, consists of an unbroken succession of discords. Most of the music of this period is in four parts. The occasional use of two-part writing may be found in Law's *Bunker Hill* (No. 47), Ingalls's *Innocent Sounds* (No. 67), Wood's *Worcester* (No. 52), and Jenks's *Evening Shade* (a three-part fuging tune, No. 61).

The melodic lines are the result of horizontal part-writing, and they are usually completely singable in spite of the dissonant clashes resulting from the meeting of independent melodic strands. The principal melody or tune is in the tenor, except in fuging sections, where all voices share the tune. The other voice parts often vary in their melodic interest, the counter (alto) sometimes serving only to complete the harmony. The treble and sometimes the counter may take on the character of a descant with the tenor, and the bass, while serving its harmonic function, not infrequently provides an agreeable melodic line. The bass part was sometimes doubled in octaves, particularly by Billings, and it is quite possible that a cello ("bass viol") was used to play the lower notes.

In the late 18th century, stringed and woodwind instruments were used to accompany the singing in churches as well as performances of secular music. There were however, few organs in the churches in Boston during this time, and most of these were in the Episcopal churches.

Voice ranges vary considerably. Whereas the treble voice rarely exceeds an octave and does not go higher than g^2, the counter has the smallest range—usually a fourth or fifth. The tenor and bass have the widest range, not infrequently an eleventh or twelfth.

A considerable number of the compositions are in major keys, with G, D, and F major the most common. The natural minor is used in Law's *Bunker Hill*, Read's *Windham*, and Doolittle's *Exhortation* (No. 60). The last-named is also one of the few pieces to use the rhythmic device of two against three. Modulations to closely related keys are frequent (see the third relationship in Kimball's *Woburn*, No. 56, second section), but chromaticism is rarely encountered. The last chord often lacks the third and sometimes the fifth, and cadences may be unprepared.

Dotted rhythms are fairly common. Sometimes these are dictated by the rhythm of the text, or they may be a part of a melismatic figure, as in Kimball's *Invitation* (No. 55).

Tone-painting is frequently used to reflect the meaning of the text, or for single words. It is used appropriately in Kimball's *Invitation* on the word "fly," on the word "peace" in Kimball's *Woburn*, for "Blow ye trumpets" in Belcher's *Jubilant* (No. 59), and in many other instances.

Expression marks are rarely indicated in the music and were probably given to the singers by the leader or singing-master. *Forte* and *piano* signs are used in Belknap's *Winter* (No. 65) and Holden's *Coronation* (No. 54); *forte* and *fortissimo* in Billings's *Jargon*.

By far the most popular texts for psalm-tune and hymn settings were the paraphrases by Isaac Watts (1674–1748), who is known as the father of English hymnody. The religious poetry of John and Charles Wesley, Nahum Tate, James Relly, and many others was also set to music by the New England composers. A few compositions with secular texts are found in most tunebooks, but there is no essential difference in musical style between those

in *The Journal of the American Musicological Society*, III (1950), 286.

[2] Louis Pichierri, *Music in New Hampshire, 1623–1800*. New York: Columbia University Press, 1960.

pieces and the ones with sacred texts.

English fuging tunes, as well as psalm-tunes, hymns, and anthems, were known in New England some years before Billings published his first collection, *The New-England Psalm-Singer,* in Boston in 1770.

Irving Lowens has described the fuging tune as follows:

> The typical American fuging tune usually begins with a homophonic section in the course of which a definite cadence is reached, frequently but not always on the tonic of the key. A fresh start is then made, in which each individual voice makes its entrance in succession, the order varying according to the inclination of the composer. In this second section—which was customarily referred to as the "fuge"—some form of imitation, in most cases quite free, was utilized for a measure or two. Normally, the fuge was then repeated, thus making the whole a small, rather tightly organized ABB form.[4]

Typical fuging tunes in the *Anthology* are Morgan's *Montgomery* (No. 58), with two fuging sections, French's *Harmony* (No. 57), Kimball's *Invitation,* Jocelin's *Psalm 146* (No. 48), Belknap's *Spring* (No. 62), Edson's *Lenox* (No. 49), and Ingalls's *Northfield* (No. 68). Atypical fuging tunes are Wood's *Worcester* and Kimball's *Woburn. Worcester* begins with fuging, and then proceeds into homophony, with the sequence repeated in the second section. *Woburn* makes special use of fuging in which each part resolves on a pedal point immediately after announcing its one-measure subject. Many of the fuging tunes use a typical repeated-note figure which may be seen in Edson's vigorous *Lenox,* Jocelin's *Psalm 146,* and others. Jenks's *Evening Shade,* a modified form of fuging tune, was one of those that found their way into Southern folk hymnody.

The writing of canons was a popular diversion, and Billings wrote several, of which the serious *When Jesus Wept* (No. 42), composed when he was twenty-two, is extraordinarily successful.

[4] Irving Lowens, "The Origins of the American Fuging Tune," *Journal of the American Musicological Society,* VI (1953), 46.

The anthem differs from the psalm-tune and hymn in length and form and may have either a religious or a secular text, although Billings defines it as "a divine song, generally in prose." Secular anthems by Lyon, Billings, Read, and Shaw are included in this chapter of the *Anthology*. They are all extended compositions, consisting of several sections that are unrelated thematically. Written for mixed voices, they include two-, three-, and four-part writing, occasional "solo" parts (sung by several voices), and chordal and imitative fuging textures. Tone-painting, including quickly changing moods and irregular meters, is often employed. William Billings's entertaining anthem *Modern Music* (No. 45) has a variety of time signatures, with the half note approximately equal to 60 MM, the quarter note equal to 120 MM, and in the final $\frac{6}{4}$ the dotted half note equal to about 80 MM. This amusing piece is in Billings's best homophonic style with almost no fuging. It clearly reflects the meaning and spirit of the text and must indeed have been a popular number at singing schools and concerts.

Down steers the Bass (1785), an anthem in praise of music by Daniel Read (No. 51), is composed to a text that had been set by Billings in 1781 under the title of *Consonance.* Read, like Billings, portrays in music the sense of the words ("Down steers the bass"; "up the treble mounts"; "mix in close embrace"). Separate words such as "warbling" and "rolls" are also imitated in the music. The first part of Read's setting is in two-, three-, and four-part writing; the last section, beginning "And sympathetic strains," makes considerable use of fuging.

Oliver Shaw's *Thanksgiving Anthem* (No. 69) was "composed and arranged for a choir of Singers, with symphonies and interludes for instruments, *ad libertum* [*sic*], and for the piano forte or organ." Although independent parts are not indicated, it may be assumed that the four instruments (clarinet and three strings) would support the voices throughout. The contrast of *forte* and *piano* is achieved not only through the usual use of "P" and "F" symbols, but also by lightening the texture through pairing the voices. The indications "dolce" and "expressivo [*sic*]," rare in music of this period, are also used. This English-influenced anthem includes a short bass solo and a "Hallelujah" ending, characteristic of many compositions of the time and later.

The term "set piece" was generally applied to music that was composed especially for a particular text and that, in contrast to psalm-tunes and hymns, could not be properly sung with another text. The texts of set pieces might be sacred or secular, and irregular meters were often employed. Among the set pieces in this chapter, although not identified as such, is Andrew Law's *Bunker Hill* (No. 47).

The fuging tunes had for many years been under criticism in England, and even at the height of their popularity in America toward the end of the 18th century the seeds of dissatisfaction were being sown. Ministers contended that "fuging tunes pall the senses and cease to excite admiration,"[5] and Samuel Holyoke, who included only a few fuging tunes in his *Harmonia Sacra* (Boston, 1791), wrote:

> The principal reason why few fuging tunes were inserted was the trifling effect produced by that sort of music; for the parts falling in, one after another each conveying a different idea, confound the sense, and render the performance a mere jargon of words.

Professionally trained European musicians were coming to America in increasing numbers and soon there seemed no longer to be any place for the rough-hewn New England school of composers. After flourishing for three decades, their music went out of fashion and gave way to a new era led by Lowell Mason and the European professional musicians. The music of the New Englanders, however, was not lost. It found its way to the West and South; much of it was preserved in Southern folk hymnody, and it is being heard again today.

[5] Ezra Weld, *A Sermon Preached at a Singing Lecture*, Springfield, 1789, as quoted by Allen P. Britton, *Theoretical Introductions in American Tune-Books to 1800* . . . Unpublished Ph.D. dissertation, University of Michigan, 1949, p. 113.

38. MY DAYS HAVE BEEN SO WONDROUS FREE

1759

Songs (MS, 1759)
Francis Hopkinson

Francis Hopkinson
(1737–1791)

glid - ing
wa - ters
if a
Tear of
mine in
creas'd their

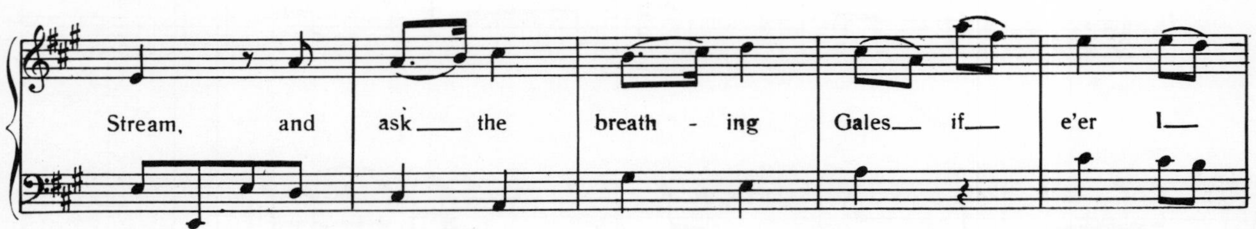
Stream, and
ask the
breath - ing
Gales if
e'er I

lent a
Sigh to
them,
I
lent a

Symphony
tr
Sigh to
them.

tr

39. A TOAST

1778

The Pennsylvania Packet (*April 8, 1778*)

Francis Hopkinson (1737–1791)

1.'Tis WASH - ING-TON'S Health fill a bump - er a - round, For— he is our
2.'Tis WASH - ING-TON'S Health loud— can - nons should roar, And— trum- pets the
3.'Tis WASH - ING-TON'S Health our— He - ro to bless, May— heav - en look

glo - ry and pride; Our— arms shall in bat - tle with con - quest be crown'd,—Whilst
truth should pro - claim; There— can - not be found.— search all the world o'er,— His
gra - cious — ly down; Oh! — long may he live— our hearts to pos - sess,— And

vir - tue and he's— on our side. Our— arms shall in bat - tle with con - quest be
e - qual in vir - tue and fame. There— can - not be found,— search all the world
free-dom still call— him her own. Oh! — long may he live— our hearts to pos -

crown'd,—Whilst vir - tue and he's on our side,— and he's— on our side.
o'er,— His e - qual in vir - tue and fame,— in vir - tue and fame.
sess,— And free - dom still call him her own,— still call— him her own.

1) [1]

[1] D in the original.

Francis Hopkinson (1778)

40. WHITEFIELD'S

1761

Urania
James Lyon
(*Philadelphia, 1761*)

Tune: *God Save the King* (1744)

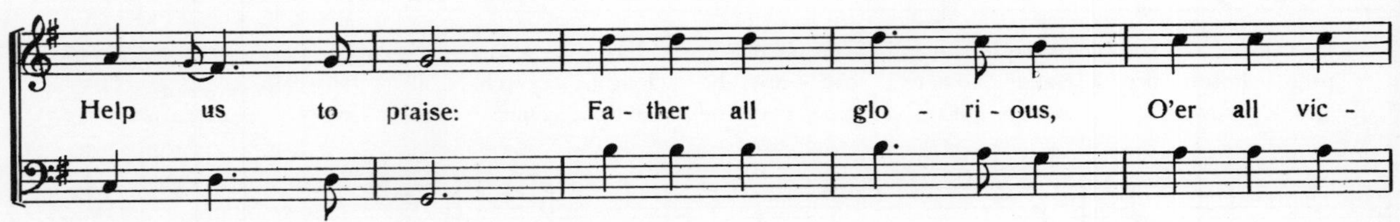

2

Jesus our Lord, arise,
Scatter our enemies,
And make them fall:
Let thine almighty aid,
Our sure defence be made,
Our souls on thee be staid:
Lord, hear our call.

3

Come holy comforter,
Thy sacred witness bear,
In this glad hour:
Thou, who almighty art,
Descend in every heart,
And ne'er from us depart,
Spirit of power.

From George Whitefield's Hymn Collection (1757)

41. FRIENDSHIP

An Ode

1774

Gentleman and Lady's Musical Companion
John Stickney
(*Newburyport, 1774*)

James Lyon
(1735–1794)

[1] In later editions.

[2] "Mourn" in later editions.
[3] In later editions.

Horae Lyricae: Isaac Watts (1706)
(1674–1748)

42. A CANON OF 4 IN 1

When Jesus Wept

1770

The New-England Psalm-Singer
William Billings
(*Boston, 1770*)

William Billings
(1746–1800)

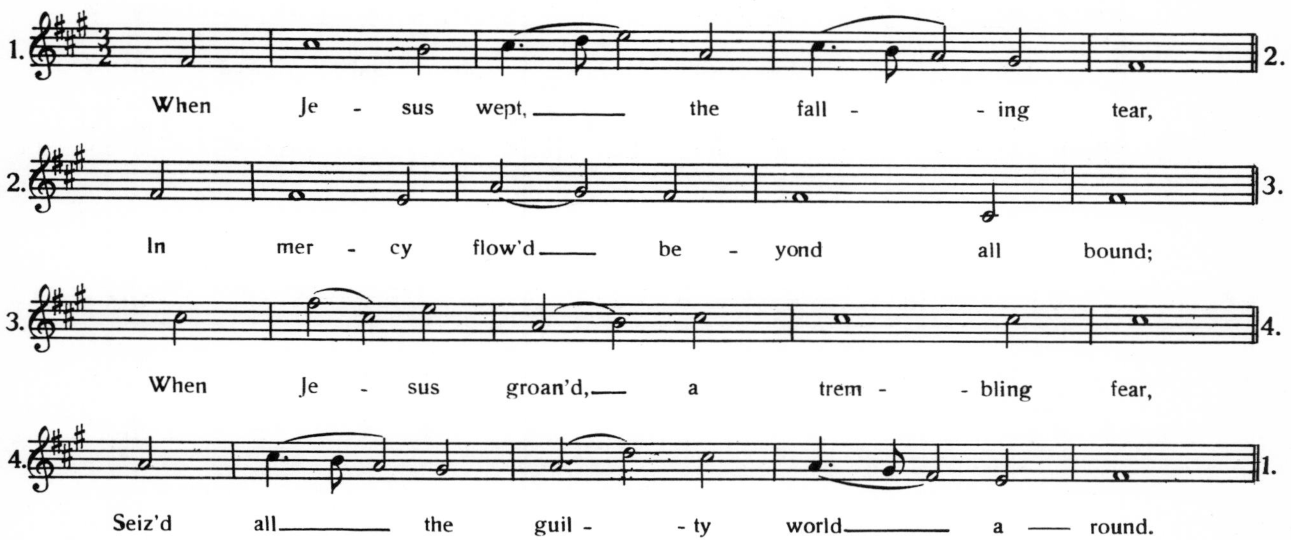

This canon may be sung by four men's voices, four women's voices, or by mixed voices. It should conclude when each voice has sung the four lines of the melody through twice, the voices dropping out in turn.

43. CHESTER

1770

The Singing-Master's Assistant
William Billings
(*Boston, 1778*)

William Billings
(1746–1800)

2

Howe and Burgoyne and Clinton too,
With Prescot and Cornwallis join'd,
Together plot our Overthrow
In one Infernal league combin'd.

3

When God inspir'd us for the fight,
Their ranks were broke, their lines were forc'd,
Their Ships were Shelter'd in our sight,
Or swiftly driven from our Coast.

4

The Foe comes on with haughty Stride,
Our troops advance with martial noise,
Their Vet'runs flee before our Youth,
And Gen'rals yield to beardless Boys.

5

What grateful Off'ring shall we bring,
What shall we render to the Lord?
Loud Hallelujahs let us Sing,
And praise his name on ev'ry Chord.

William Billings

44. JARGON

1778

The Singing-Master's Assistant
William Billings
(*Boston, 1778*)

William Billings
(1746–1800)

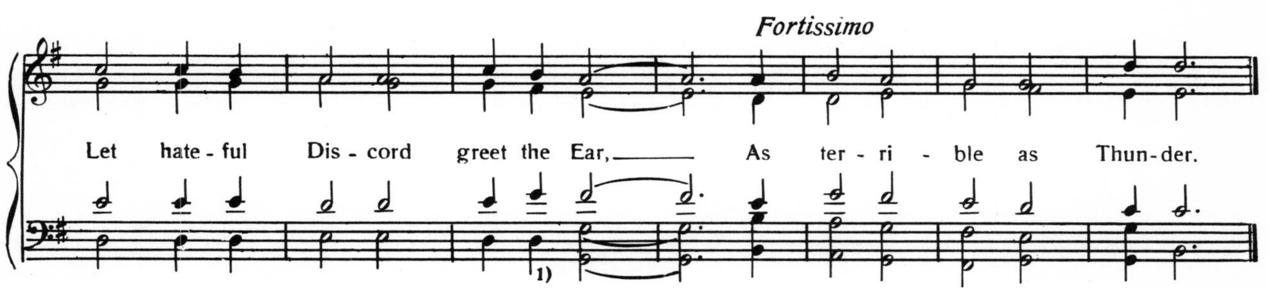

[1] C may have been intended here.

William Billings

45. MODERN MUSIC

1781

The Psalm-Singer's Amusement
William Billings
(*Boston, 1781*)

William Billings
(1746–1800)

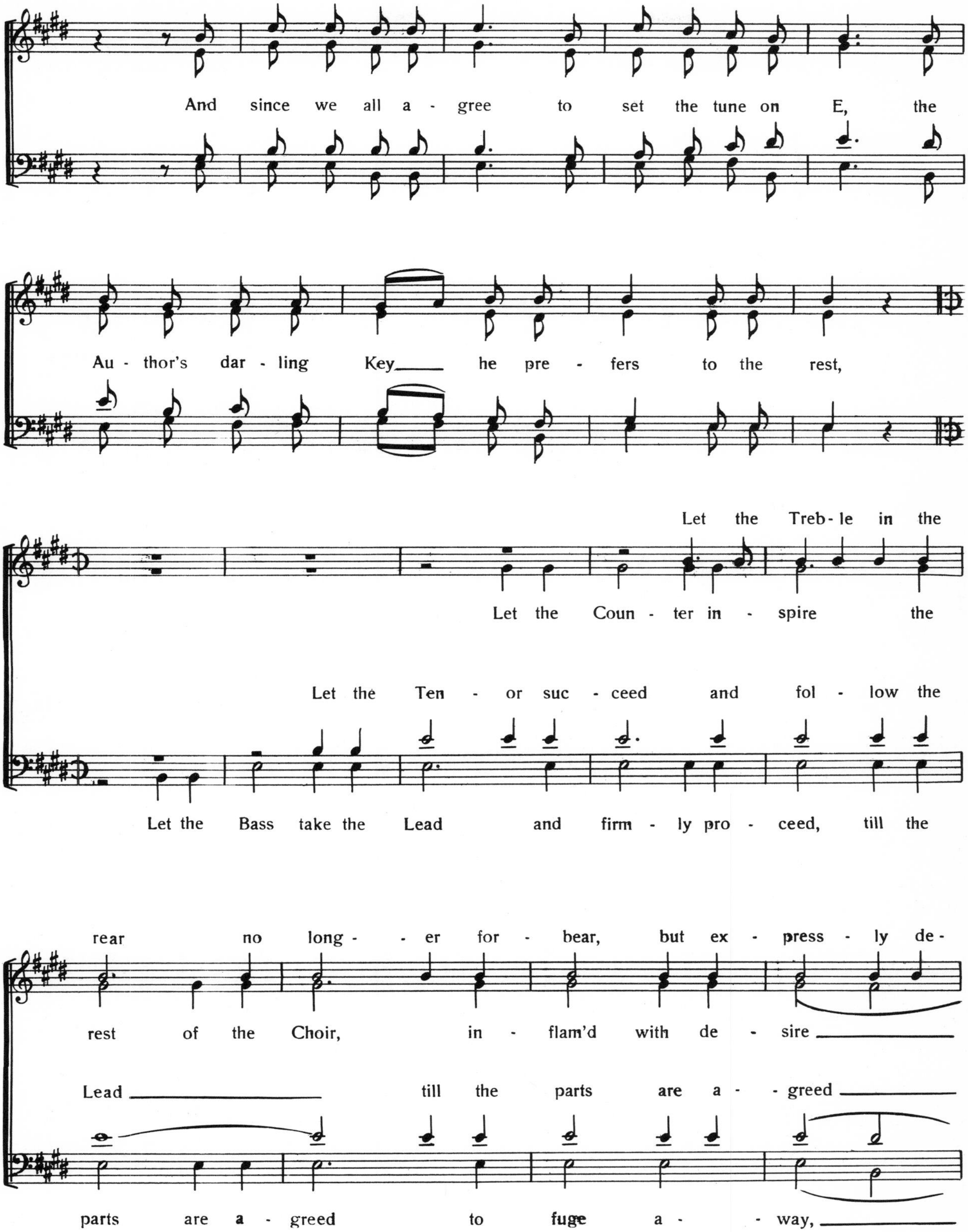

And since we all a - gree to set the tune on E, the
Au - thor's dar - ling Key he pre - fers to the rest,
Let the Treb - le in the
Let the Coun - ter in - spire the
Let the Ten - or suc - ceed and fol - low the
Let the Bass take the Lead and firm - ly pro - ceed, till the
rear no long - - er for - bear, but ex - press - ly de -
rest of the Choir, in - flam'd with de - sire
Lead till the parts are a - - greed
parts are a - greed to fuge a - - way,

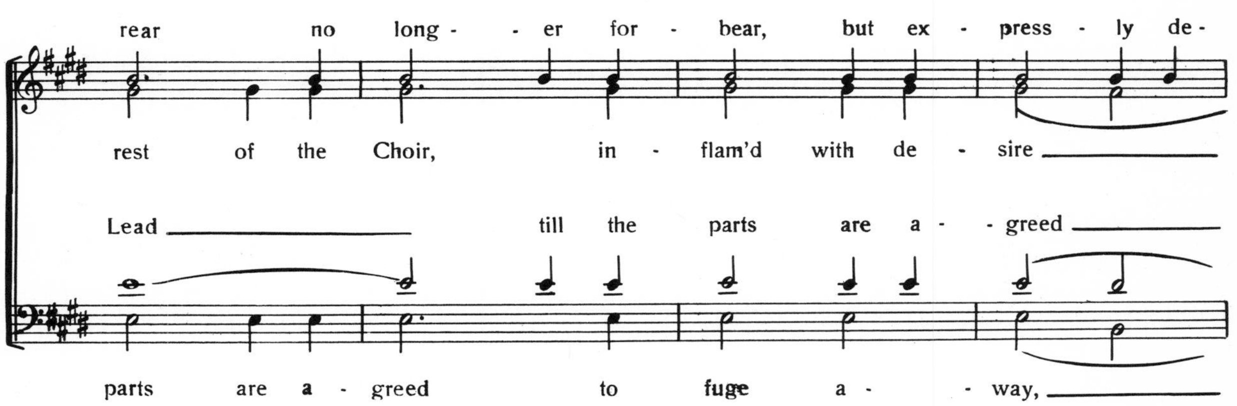

clare for a fuge a - way.
to fuge á - way.
Then change to brisk - er
to fuge a - way.
to fuge a - way.
time, and up the Lad - der climb, and down a -
gain, Then mount the sec - ond time and end the strain.
Then change the Key to pen - sive tones, and
slow in Treb - le time the Notes. Ex - ceed - ing

low keep down a - while, then rise by slow de - grees; The
pro - - cess sure - - ly will not fail to please.
Thro Common and Treb - le we jointly have run, We'el
give you their Es - sence com - pound - ed in one: All - tho we are strong-ly at -
tach'd to the rest, Six four is the move-ment that pleas-es us best, that

pleas - es us best, six four is the move-ment that pleas - es us best.
And now we ad - dress you as Friends to the cause (Per_
form - ers are_ mod - est_ and_ write their own laws) Al - tho we are san-guine and_
clap at the Bars, 'tis the part of the Hear - ers to clap their Ap - plause, to_
clap their Ap - plause, 'tis the part of the Hear - ers to clap their Ap-plause.

46. CONQUEST

1786

The Suffolk Harmony
William Billings
(*Boston, 1786*)

William Billings
(1746–1800)

James Relly
(c. 1722–1778)

47. BUNKER HILL

A Sapphick Ode

1775

From a Broadside Version
(*Norwich, Connecticut, 1775*)

Andrew Law
(1748–1821)

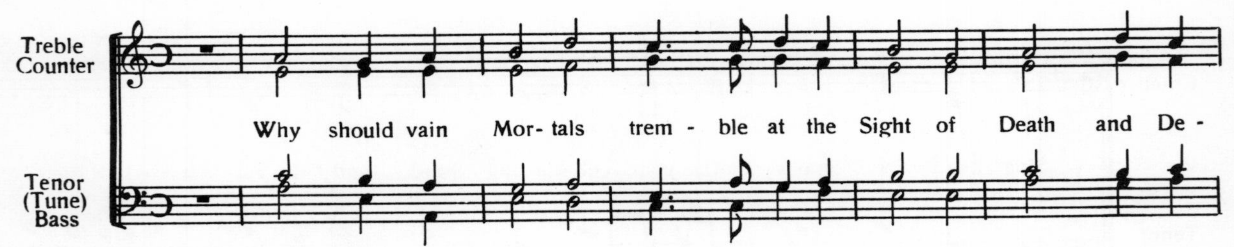

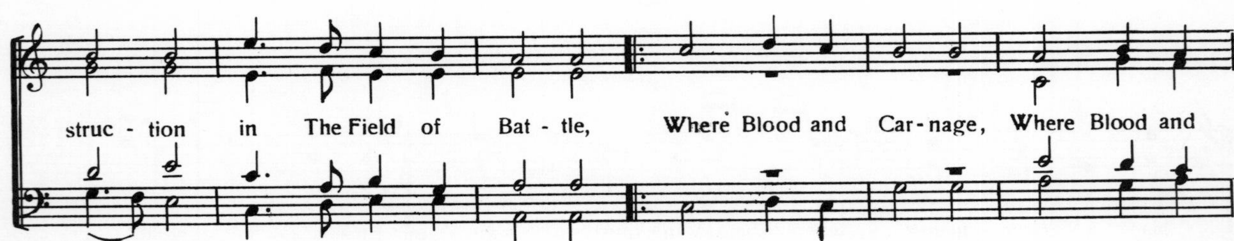

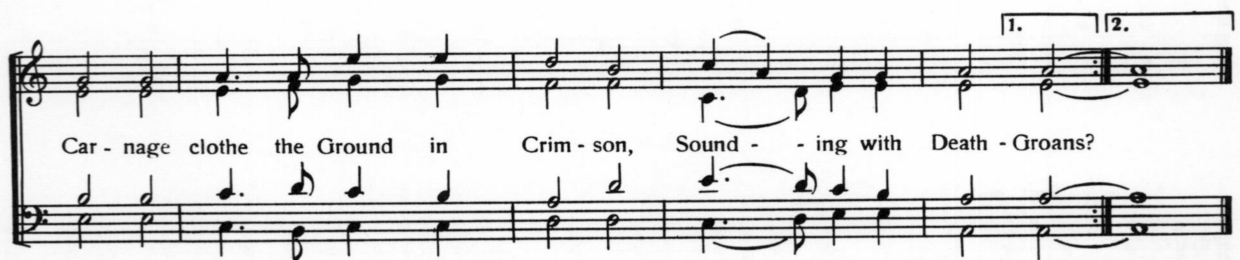

2

Death will invade us by the Means appointed,
And we must all bow to the King of Terrors;
Nor am I anxious, if I am prepared,
What shape he comes in.

8

Now, *Mars*, I dare thee, clad in smoky Pillars
Bursting from Bomb-Shells, roaring from the Cannon,
Rattling in Grape Shot, like a Storm of Hailstones,
Torturing AEther!

14

Fame and dear Freedom, *lure* me on to Battle,
While a fell Despot, grimer than a Death's-Head,
Stings me with Serpents, fiercer than Medusa's:
To the Encounter.

15

Life, for my Country and the Cause of Freedom,
Is but a Trifle for a Worm to part with;
And if preserved in so great a Contest,
Life is redoubled.

From *The American Hero* by Nathaniel Niles

48. PSALM 146

1788

The Chorister's Companion
Simeon Jocelin & Amos Doolittle
(New Haven, 1788)

Simeon Jocelin
(1746–1823)

death, Praise shall em - ploy my no - - bler powers:
8
death, Praise shall em - ploy my no - - bler powers:
My days of praise
My
8
My days of praise shall ne'er be
My days of praise shall ne'er be past,

4

The Lord hath eyes to give the blind;
The Lord supports the sinking mind;
He sends the labouring conscience peace:
He helps the stranger in distress,
The widow and the fatherless,
And grants the prisoner sweet release.

5

He loves his saints; he knows them well,
But turns the wicked down to hell;
Thy God, O Zion! ever reigns:
Let every tongue, let every age;
In this exalted work engage;
Praise him in everlasting strains.

Ps. 146: Isaac Watts (1719)
(1674–1748)

49. LENOX

1782

The Chorister's Companion
Simeon Jocelin & Amos Doolittle
(*New Haven, 1782*)

Lewis Edson, Sr.
(1748–1820)

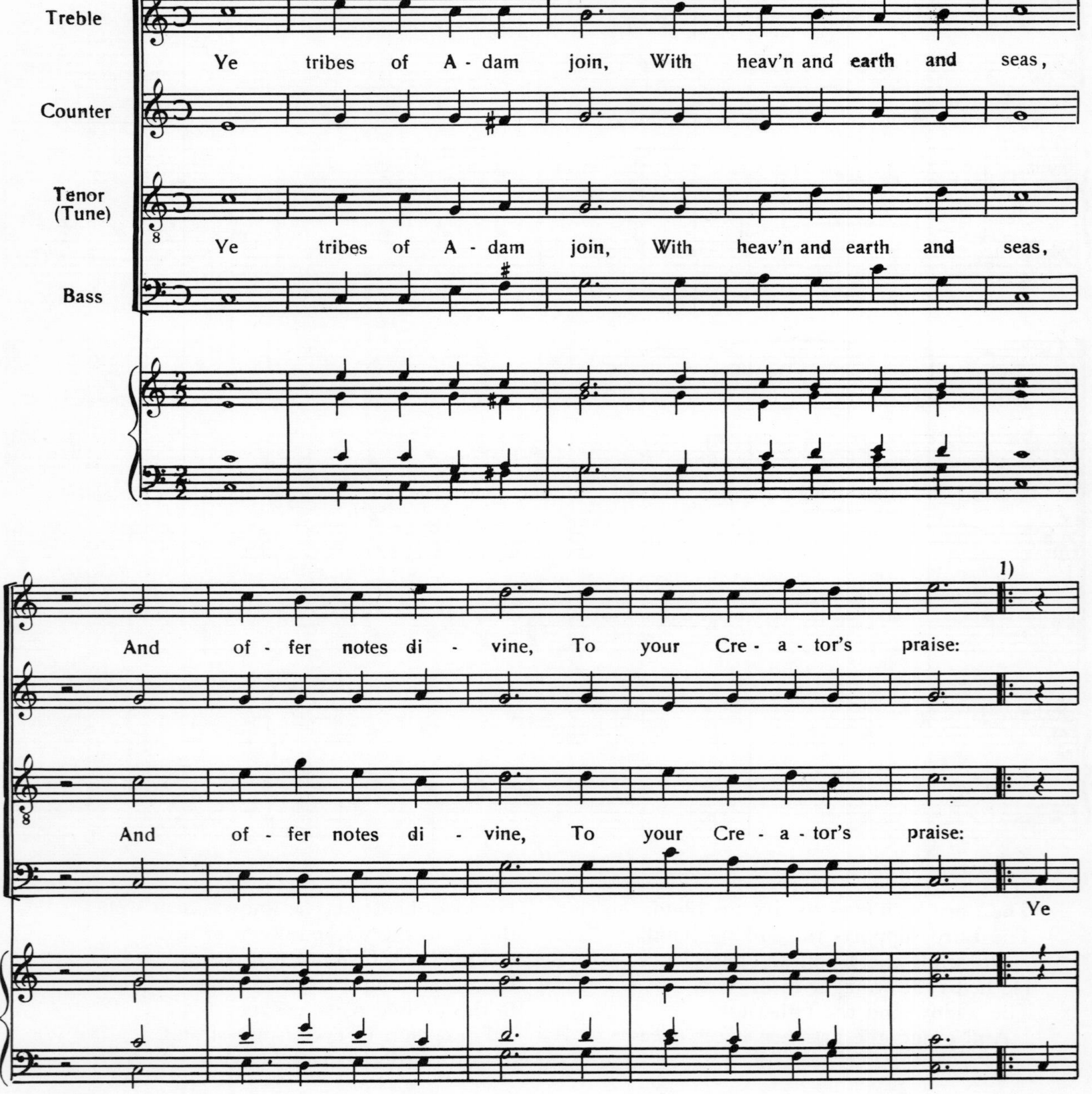

[1] The customary repeat signs appear in later editions.

[2] This note is E in the original.
[3] The note D is found in later editions.

2

Thou sun, with dazzling rays,
And moon that rules the night,
Shine to your Maker's praise,
With stars of twinkling light:
His power declare,
Ye floods on high,
And clouds that fly
In empty air.

10

Let all the nations fear
The God that rules above:
He brings his people near,
And makes them taste his love:
While earth and sky
Attempt his praise,
His saints shall raise
His honours high.

Ps. 148: Isaac Watts (1719)
(1674–1748)

50. WINDHAM

1785

The American Singing Book
Daniel Read
(New Haven, 1785)

Daniel Read
(1757–1836)

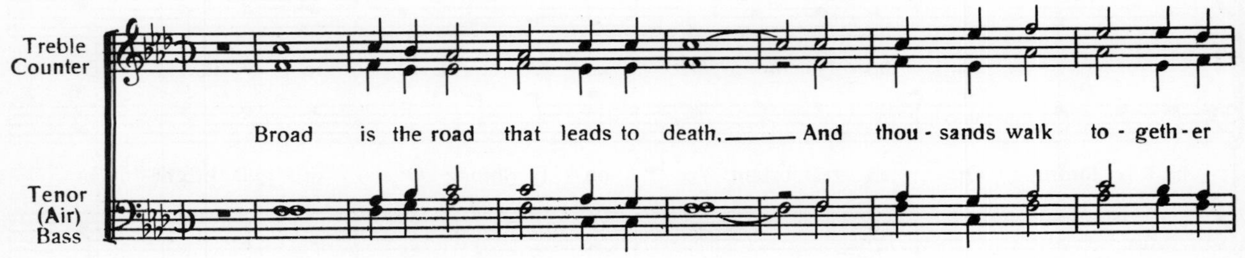

2

"Deny thyself, and take thy cross,"
Is the Redeemer's great command:
Nature must count her gold but dross,
If she would gain the heavenly land.

3

The fearful soul that tires and faints,
And walks the ways of God no more,
Is but esteem'd almost a saint,
And makes his own destruction sure.

4

Lord, let not all my hopes be vain;
Create my heart entirely new;
Which hypocrites could ne'er attain
Which false apostates never knew.

Hymn: Isaac Watts (1707)
(1674–1748)

51. AN ANTHEM

Down Steers the Bass

1785

The American Singing Book
Daniel Read
(*New Haven, 1785*)

Daniel Read
(1757–1836)

in mild Mel - o - dious Maze, Warbl - - ing be-tween the
in mild Mel - o - dious Maze, Warbl - ing be-tween, warbl -
Ten - or_ gent - ly Plays, the Ten - or gent - ly Plays, warbl - ing be -
ing be-tween the_ Ten - or gent-ly Plays, warbl - ing_ be -

tween the Ten - or gent - ly Plays: But if th'a - spir - ing
8
tween the Ten - or gent - ly Plays: But if th'a - spir - ing

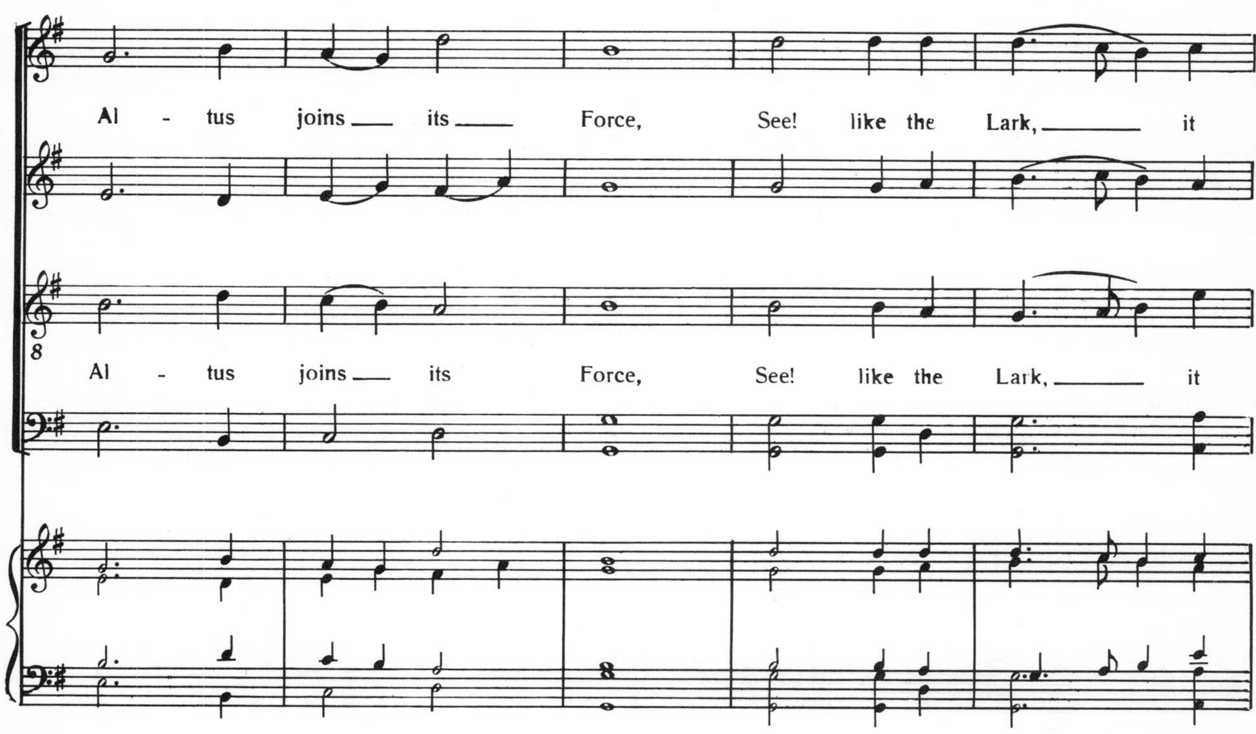
Al - tus joins its Force, See! like the Lark, it
8
Al - tus joins its Force, See! like the Lark, it

Wings its tow'r - ing Course; Through Har-mo - ny's sub - lim - est Sphere it
Wings its tow'r - ing Course; Through Har-mo - ny's sub - lim - est Sphere it

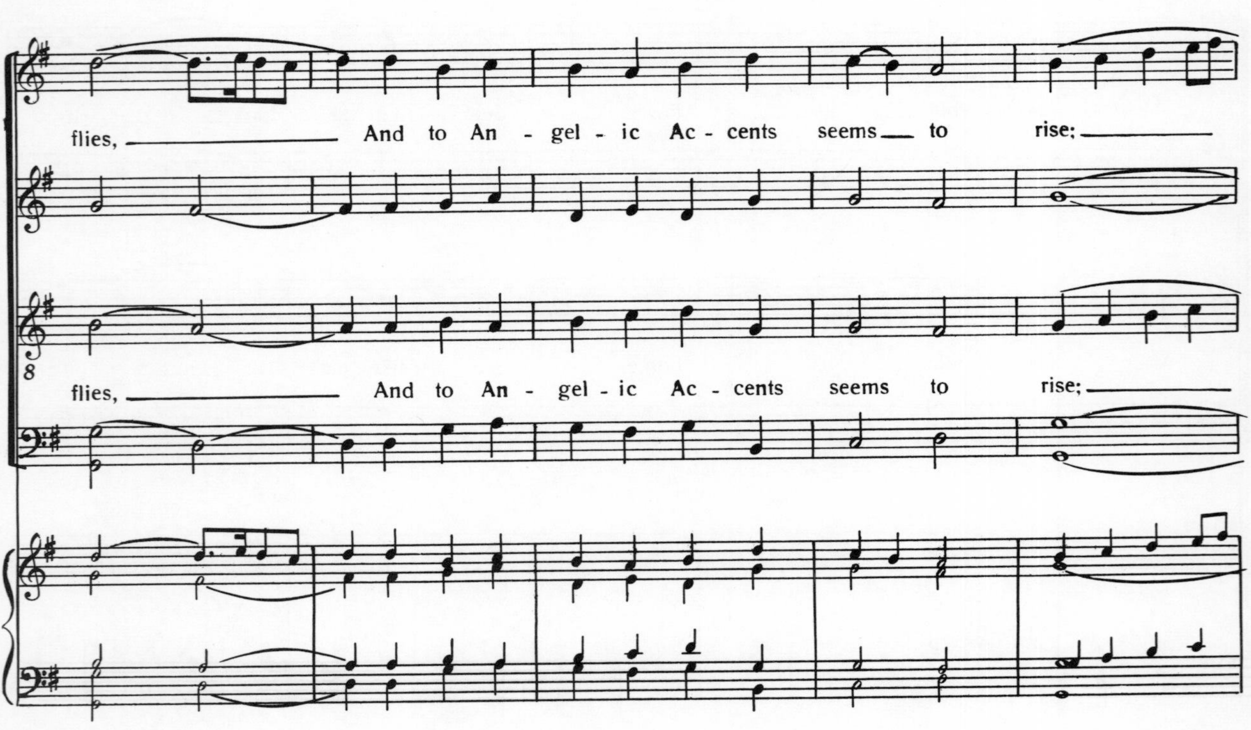
flies, And to An - gel - ic Ac - cents seems to rise;
flies, And to An - gel - ic Ac - cents seems to rise;

[1] The dynamic indications are in the original.

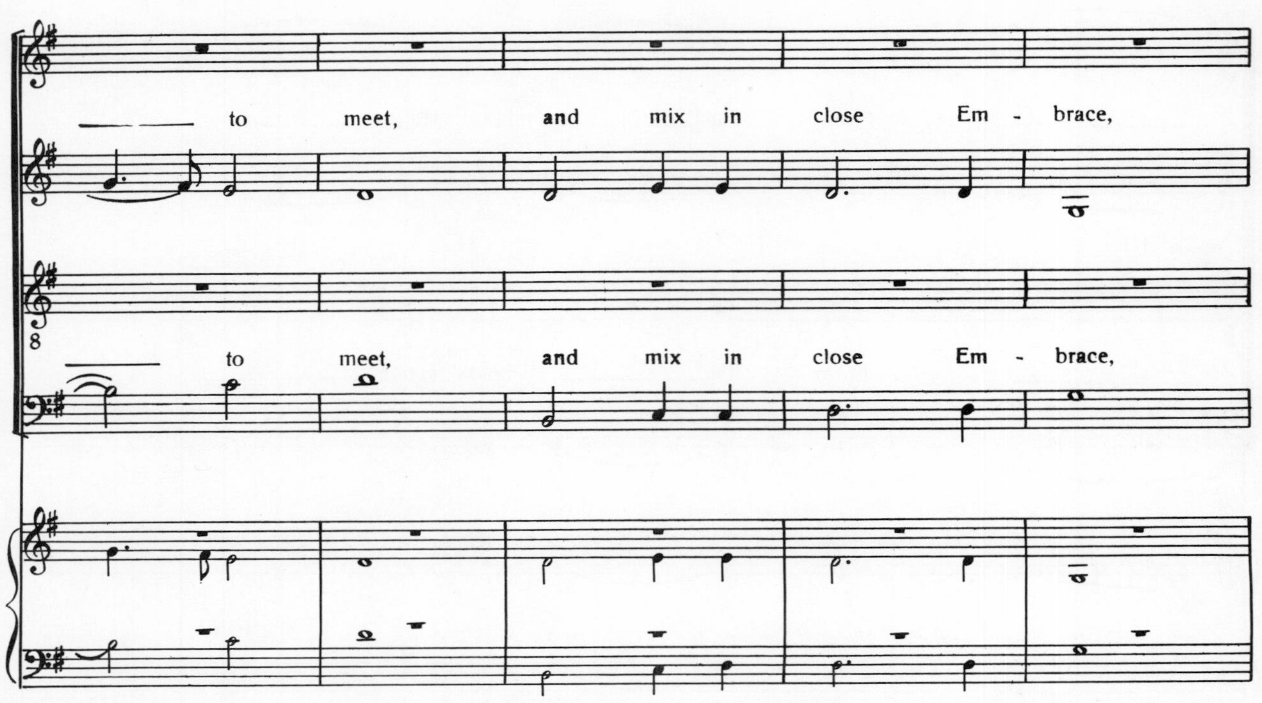
to meet, and mix in close Em - brace,
8
to meet, and mix in close Em - brace,

Through dif - f'rent Sys - tems all the Parts di - vide, With
8
Through dif - f'rent Sys - tems all the Parts di - vide. With

Mu - sick's Chords the dis - tant Notes are ty'd;
Mu - sick's Chords the dis - tant Notes are ty'd;
And

And Sym - pa - thet - ic
And Sym - pa - thet - ic Strains en - chant - - ing winde
And Sym - pa - thet - ic Strains en - chant - -
Sym - pa - thet - ic Strains en - chant - - ing winde Their rest - less

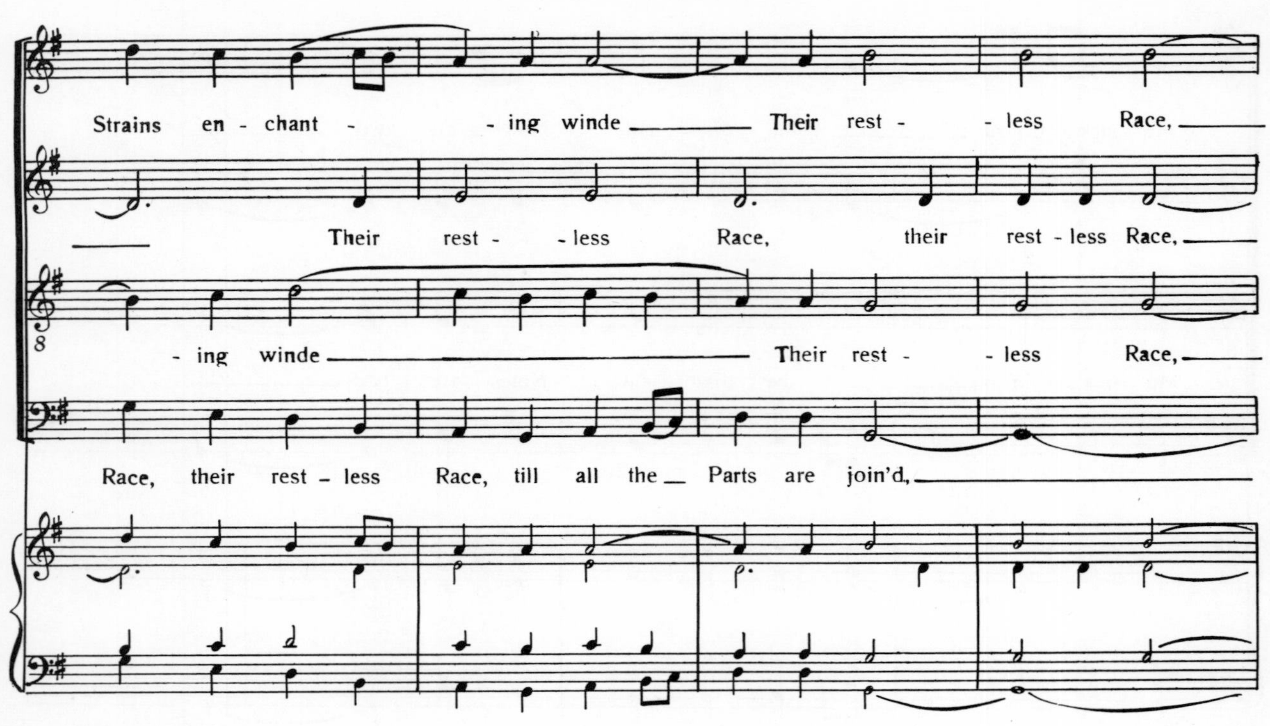
Strains en - chant - - ing winde Their rest - - less Race,
Their rest - - less Race, their rest - less Race,
- ing winde Their rest - - less Race,
Race, their rest - less Race, till all the Parts are join'd,

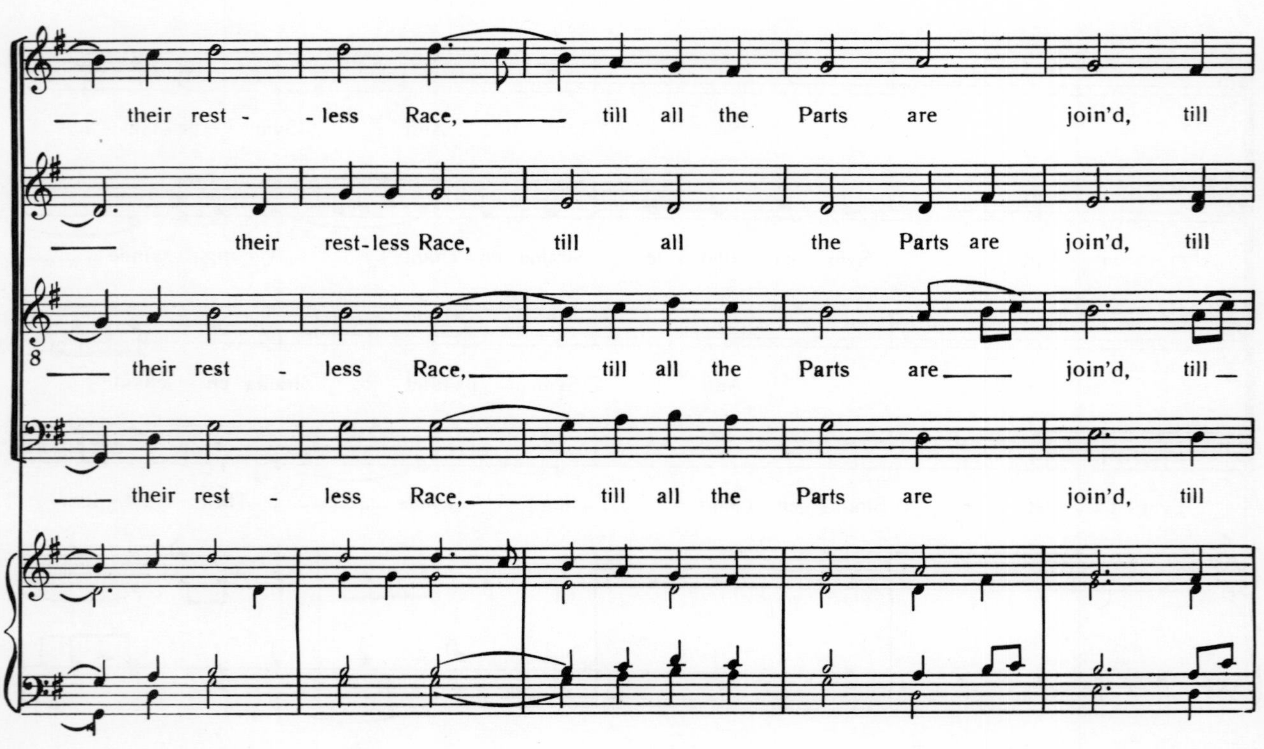
their rest - - less Race, till all the Parts are join'd, till
their rest-less Race, till all the Parts are join'd, till
their rest - less Race, till all the Parts are join'd, till
their rest - less Race, till all the Parts are join'd, till

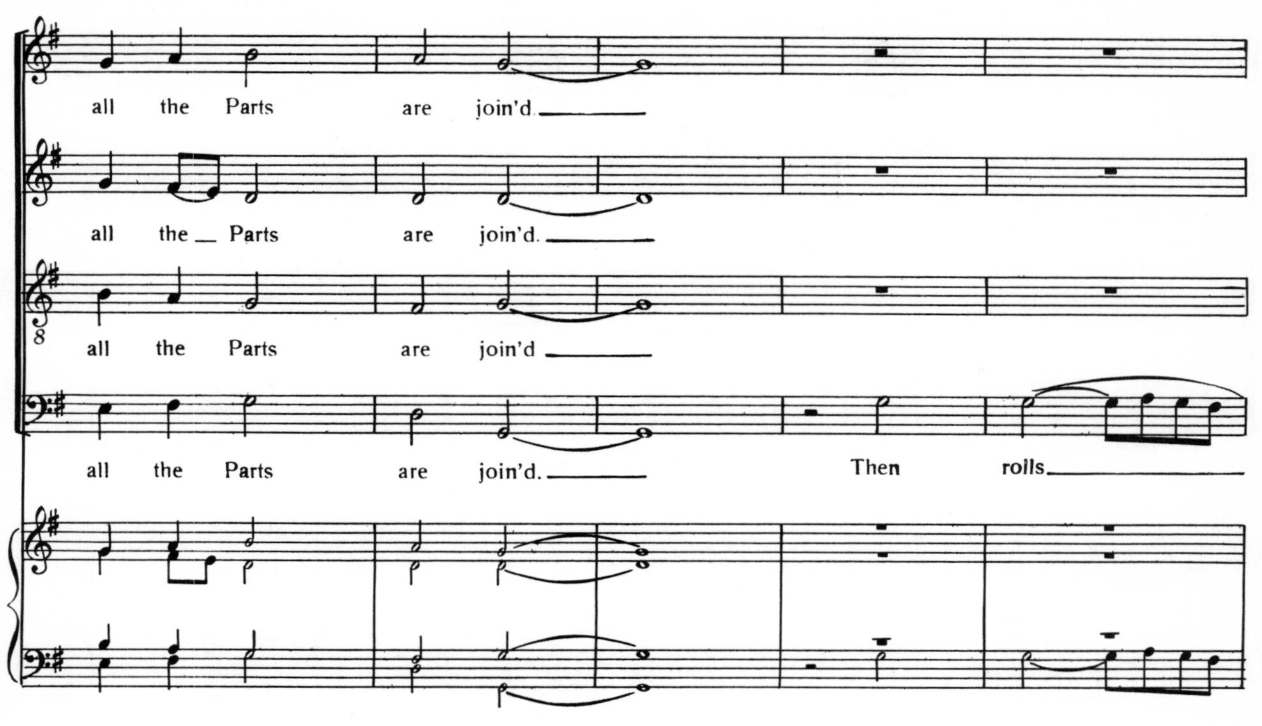
all the Parts are join'd.
all the Parts are join'd.
all the Parts are join'd
all the Parts are join'd. Then rolls

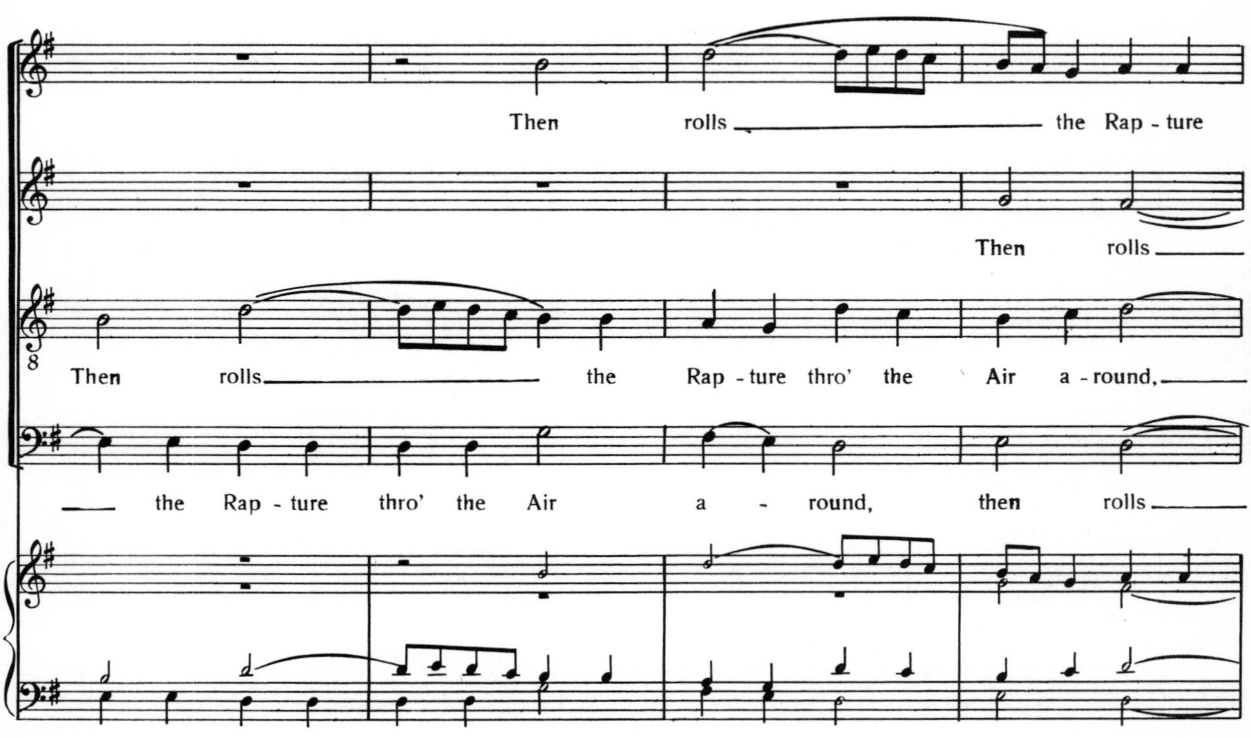
Then rolls the Rap - ture
Then rolls
Then rolls the Rap - ture thro' the Air a - round,
the Rap - ture thro' the Air a - round, then rolls

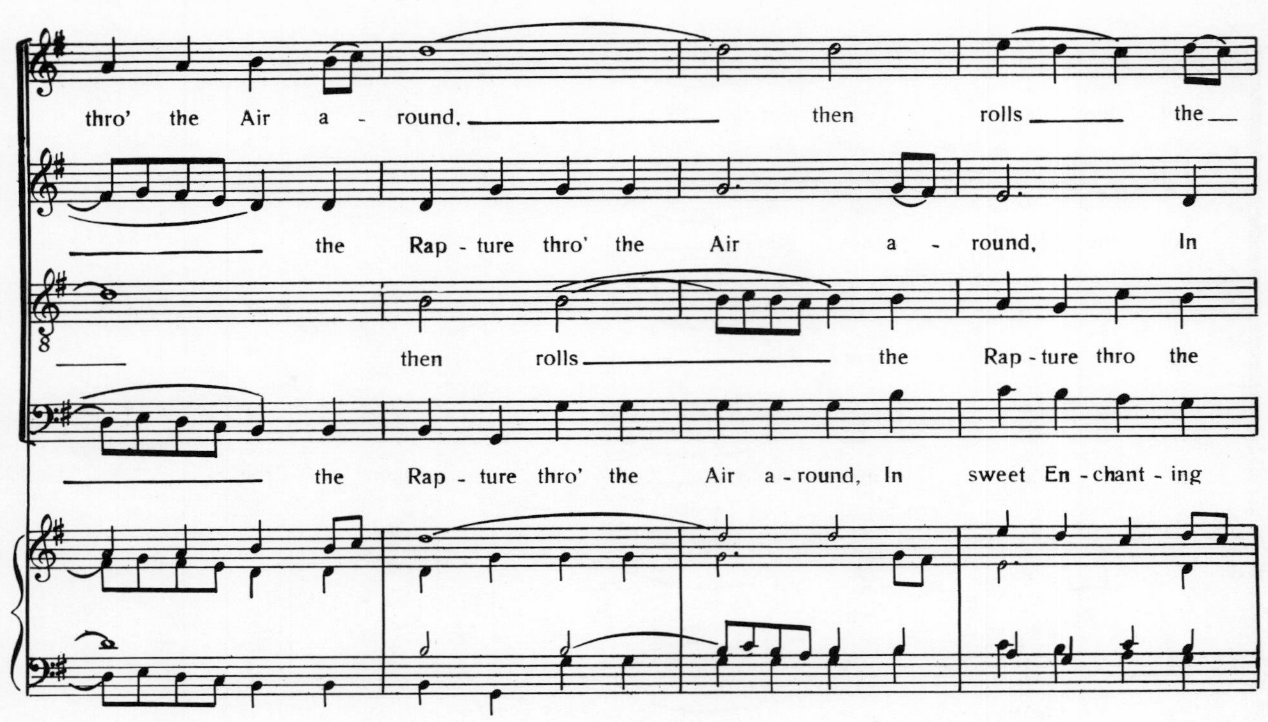
thro' the Air a - round, then rolls the
the Rap - ture thro' the Air a - round, In
then rolls the Rap - ture thro the
the Rap - ture thro' the Air a - round, In sweet En - chant - ing

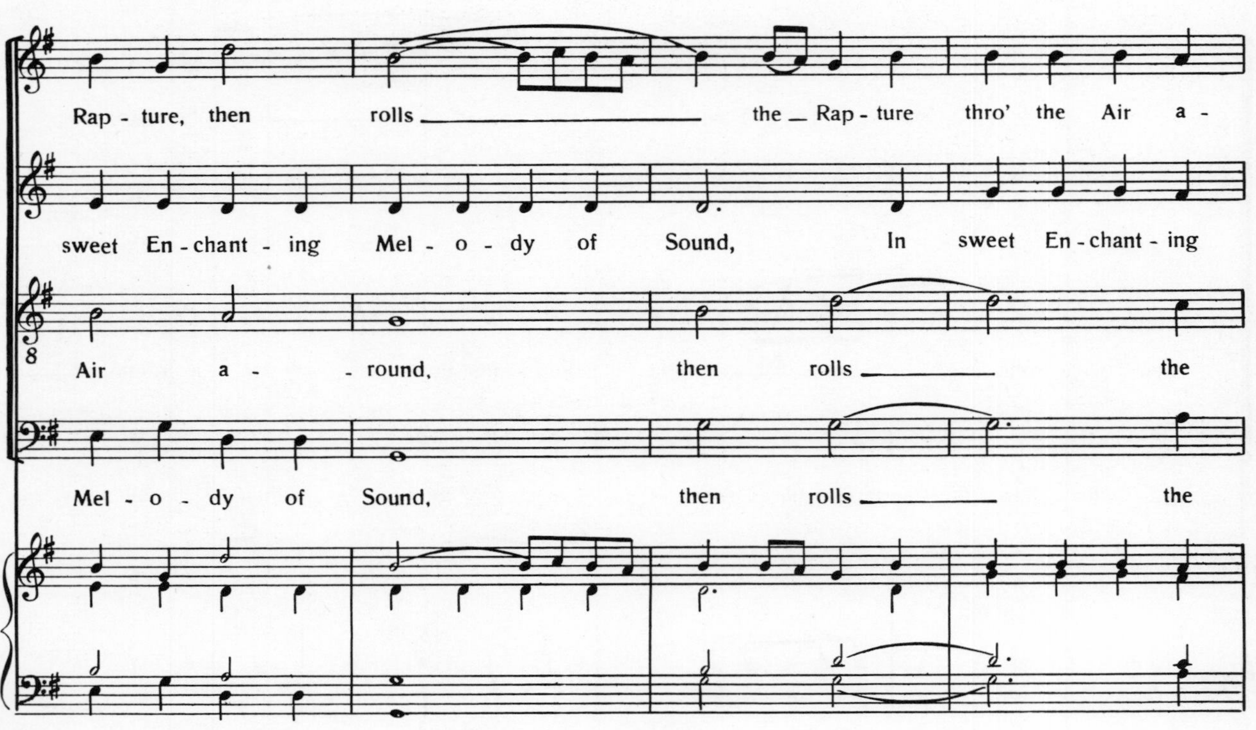
Rap - ture, then rolls the Rap - ture thro' the Air a -
sweet En - chant - ing Mel - o - dy of Sound, In sweet En - chant - ing
Air a - - round, then rolls the
Mel - o - dy of Sound, then rolls the

From a *Miscellany* of the Rev. Dr. Byles
(1706–1788)

52. WORCESTER

1786

The Worcester Collection of Sacred Harmony
Isaiah Thomas
(*Worcester, 1786*)

Abraham Wood
(1752–1804)

[1] B-flat in the original.
[2] E in the original.

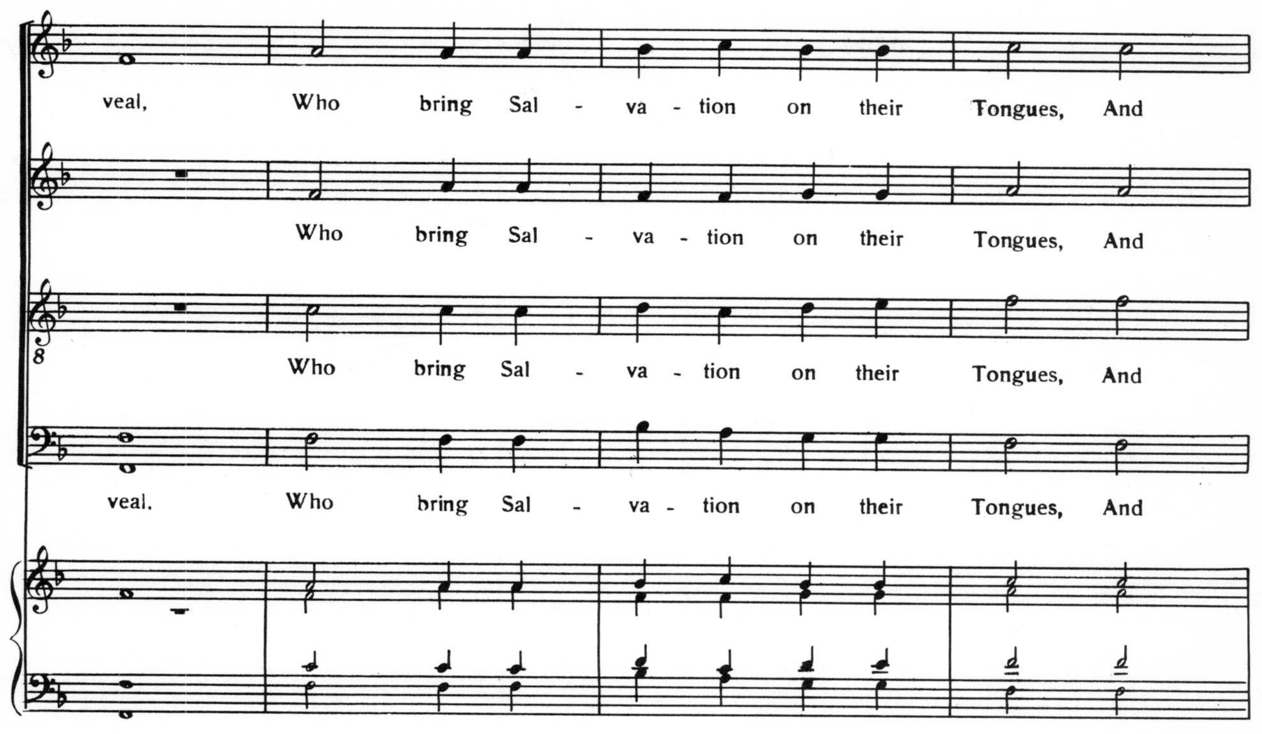
veal, Who bring Sal - va - tion on their Tongues, And
Who bring Sal - va - tion on their Tongues, And
Who bring Sal - va - tion on their Tongues, And
veal. Who bring Sal - va - tion on their Tongues, And

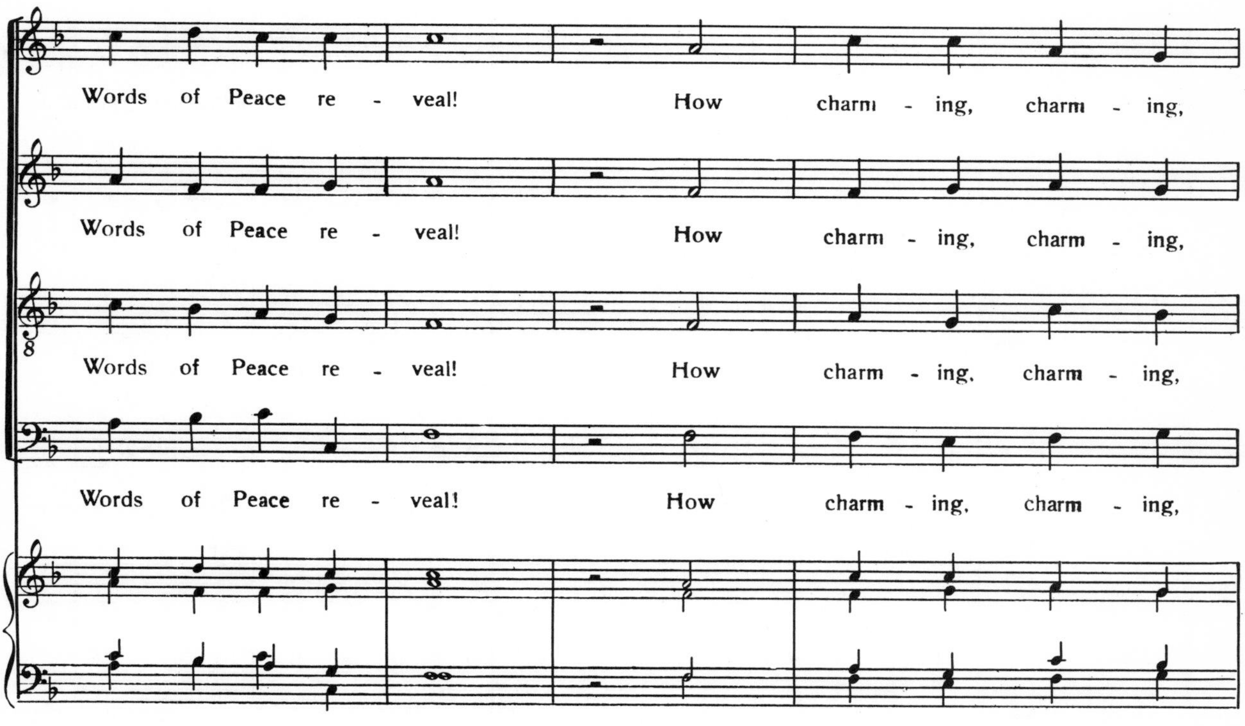
Words of Peace re - veal! How charm - ing, charm - ing,
Words of Peace re - veal! How charm - ing, charm - ing,
Words of Peace re - veal! How charm - ing, charm - ing,
Words of Peace re - veal! How charm - ing, charm - ing,

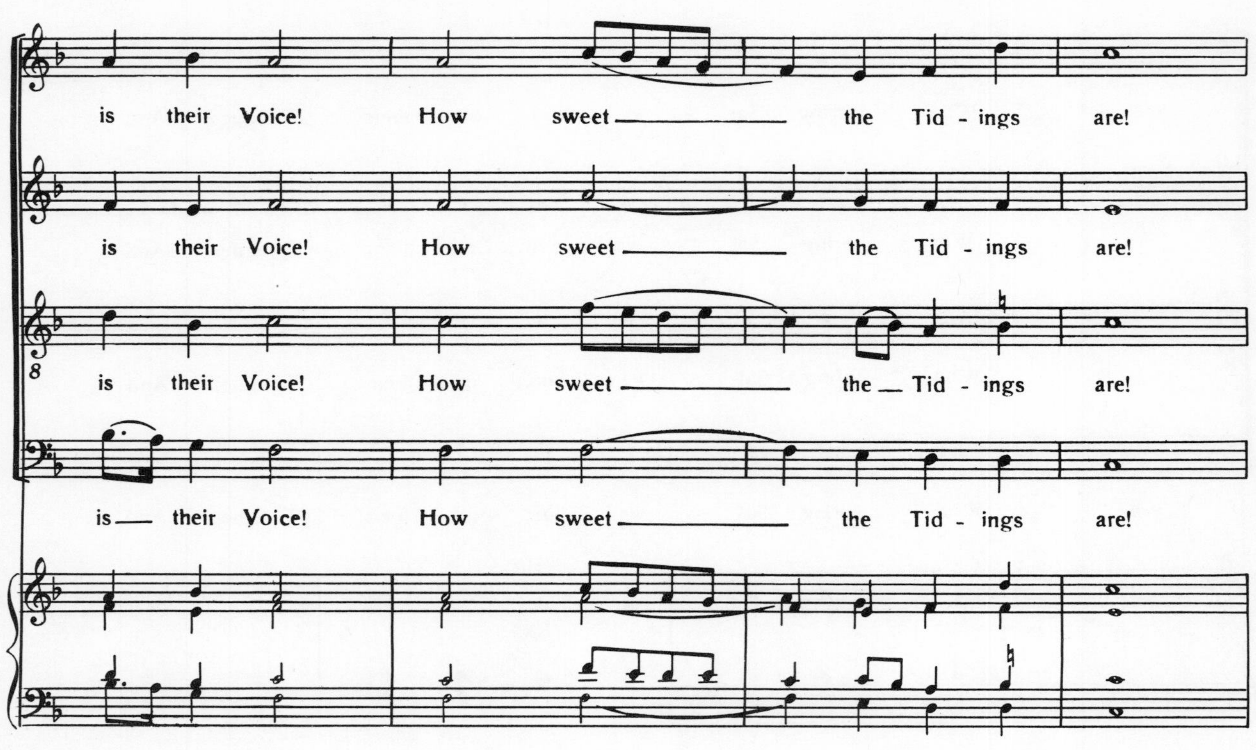
is their Voice! How sweet the Tid - ings are!
is their Voice! How sweet the Tid - ings are!
is their Voice! How sweet the — Tid - ings are!
is — their Voice! How sweet the Tid - ings are!

Zi - on, be - hold thy Sav - iour
Zi - on, be - hold thy Sav - iour King, He reigns and
Zi - on, be - hold thy Sav - iour King, He reigns and tri - umphs here,
Zi - on, be - hold thy Sav - iour King, He reigns and — tri-umphs here, Zi - on, behold thy

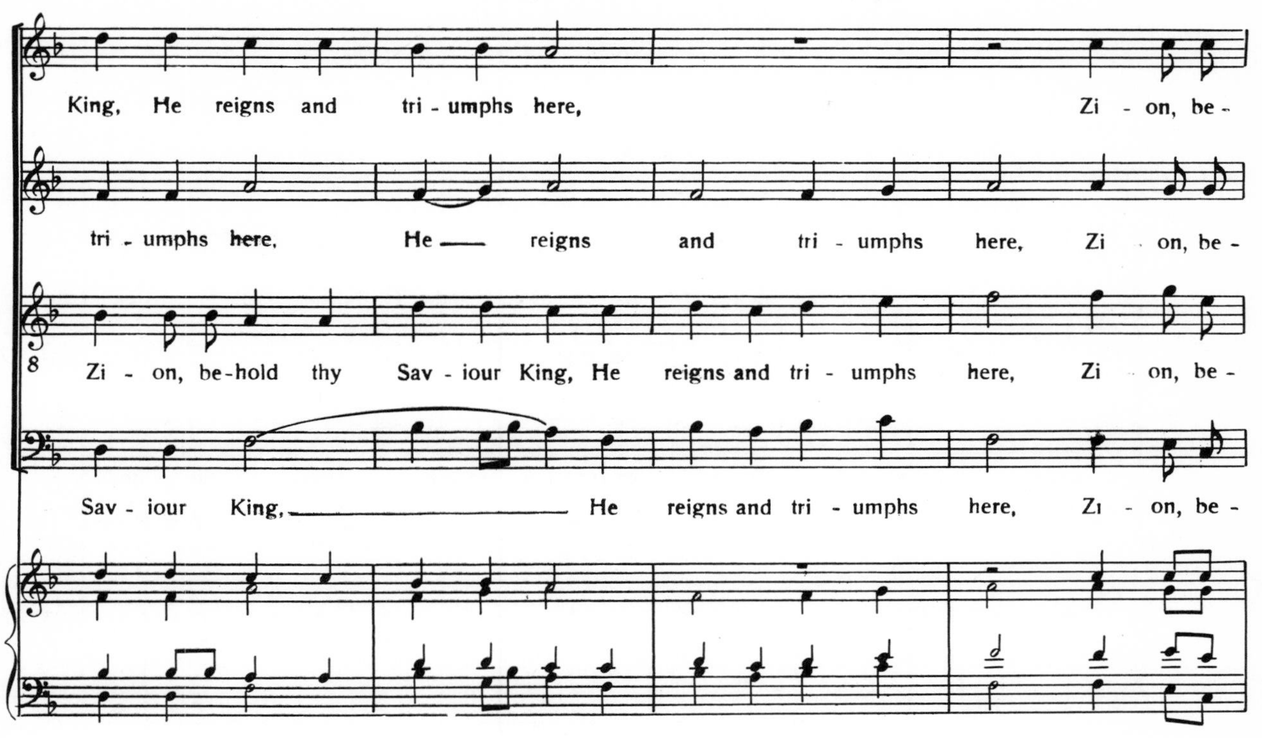

Hymn: Isaac Watts (1707)
(1674–1748)

53. CHINA

1790

The New England Harmony
Timothy Swan
(*Northampton, 1801*)

Timothy Swan
(1758–1842)

2

Are we not tending upward too,
As fast as time can move?
Nor would we wish the hours more slow
To keep us from our love.

6

Then let the last loud trumpet sound,
And bid our kindred rise;
Awake, ye nations, under ground;
Ye saints, ascend the skies.

Hymn: Isaac Watts (1707)
(1674–1748)

54. CORONATION

1793

The Union Harmony
Oliver Holden
(*Boston, 1793*)

Oliver Holden
(1765–1844)

2

Crown him, ye martyrs of our God,
Who from his altar call;
Extol the stem of Jesse's rod,
And crown him Lord of all.

5

Let every kindred, every tribe,
On this terrestrial ball,
To him all majesty ascribe,
And crown him Lord of all.
Edward Perronet (1779)
(1726–1792)

55. INVITATION

1793

The Rural Harmony
Jacob Kimball
(*Boston, 1793*)

Jacob Kimball
(1761–1826)

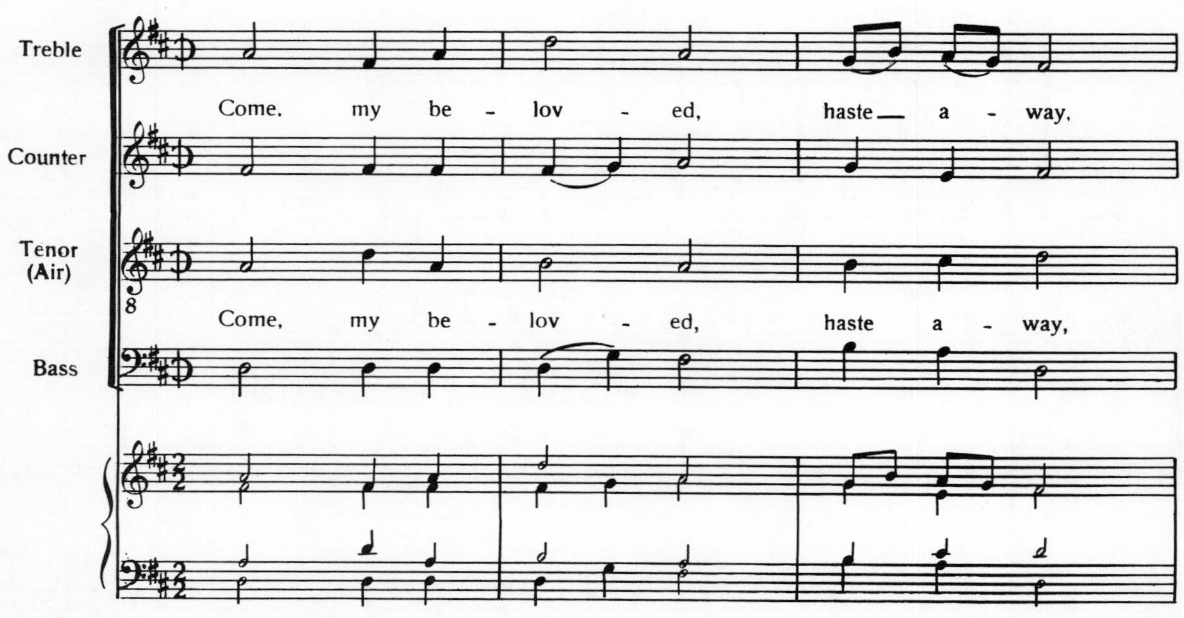

Roe, O - ver the hills where spic - es grow.
Roe, O - ver the hills where spic - es grow.
Fly like a
8
Fly like a youth - ful Hart
Fly like a
Fly like a youth - ful Hart or Roe, O - ver the
youth - ful Hart or Roe, O - ver the hills where spic -
8

or Roe, O - - ver the hills where spic - es
youth - ful Hart or Roe, O - - ver the hills where spic - es
hills where spic - es grow, Fly like a youth - ful Hart or Roe,
- es grow, Fly like a youth - ful Hart or Roe,

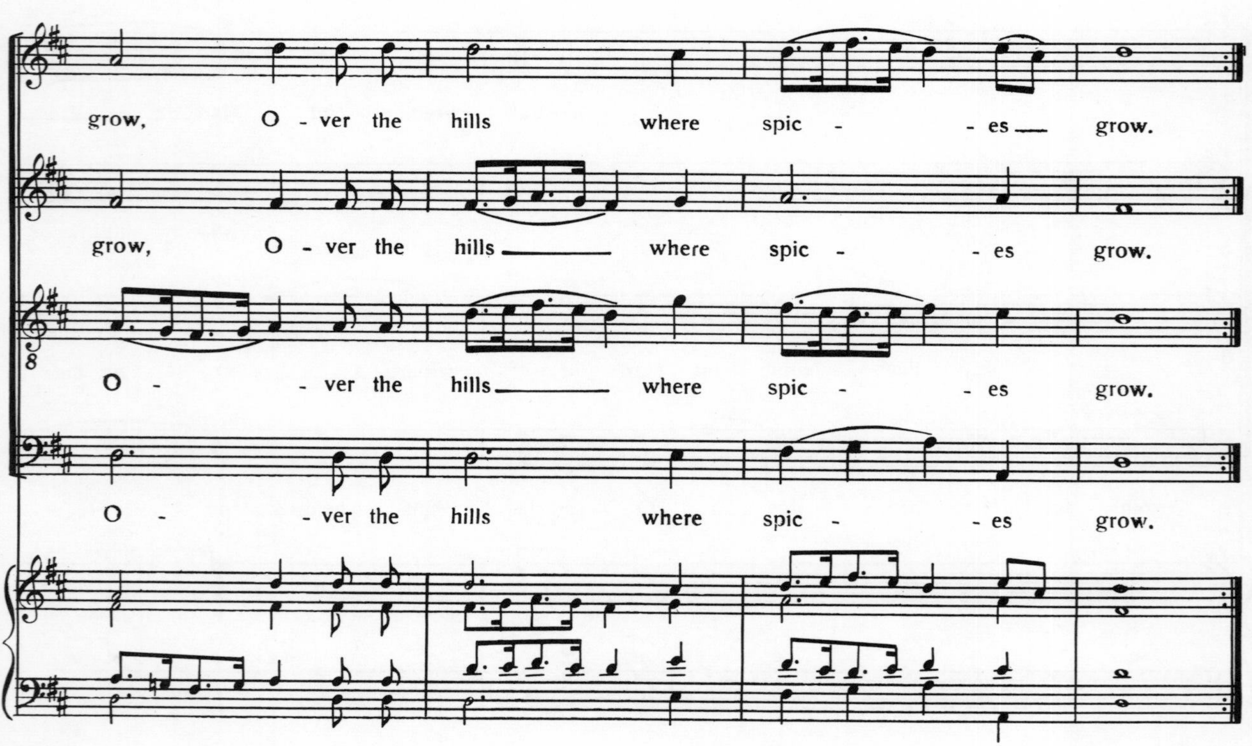
grow, O - ver the hills where spic - es grow.
grow, O - ver the hills where spic - es grow.
O - ver the hills where spic - es grow.
O - ver the hills where spic - es grow.

56. WOBURN

1793

The Rural Harmony
Jacob Kimball
(*Boston, 1793*)

Jacob Kimball
(1761–1826)

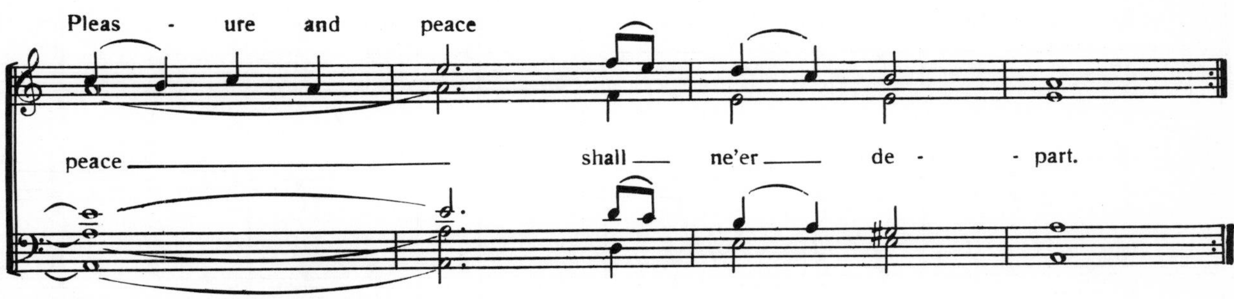

Ps. 30: Isaac Watts (1719)
(1674–1748)

57. HARMONY

1793

The Psalmodist's Companion
Jacob French
(*Northampton, 1793*)

Jacob French
(b. 1754)

word, And sound it dread - - ful down to hell.
word, And sound it dread - - ful down to hell. The
The Lord, how ab - so -
The Lord, how ab - so - lute he reigns! Let ev - ery an - gel
The Lord, how ab - so - lute he reigns! Let
Lord, how ab - so - lute he reigns! Let ev - ery an - gel bend the knee, bend,
- lute he reigns! Let ev - ery an - gel bend the knee, bend, bend the knee:

11

Jehovah! 'tis a glorious word;
O may it dwell on every tongue!
But saints, who best have known the Lord,
Are bound to raise the noblest song.

12

Speak of the wonders of that love
Which Gabriel plays on every chord;
From all below, and all above,
Loud hallelujahs to the Lord!

Ps. 148: Isaac Watts (1719)
(1674–1748)

58. MONTGOMERY

1793

Union Harmony
Oliver Holden
(*Boston, 1793*)

Justin Morgan
(1747–1798)

[1] A in the original.

²D in the original.

Ps. 63: Isaac Watts (1719)
(1674–1748)

59. JUBILANT

1794

The Harmony of Maine
Supply Belcher
(*Boston, 1794*)

Supply Belcher
(1751–1836)

[1] E in the original.

60. EXHORTATION

1800

The Easy Instructor
Wm. Little & Wm. Smith
(*Albany, c. 1809*)

Eliakim Doolittle
(1772–1850)

[1] These two eighth notes are A and B in the original.

2

Behold the aged sinner goes,
Laden with guilt and heavy woes,
Down to the regions of the dead,
With endless curses on his head.

4

Eternal King! I fear thy name;
Teach me to know how frail I am:
And when my soul must hence remove,
Give me a mansion in thy love.

Hymn: Isaac Watts (1707)
(1674–1748)

61. EVENING SHADE

1805

Norfolk Compiler
Stephen Jenks
(*Dedham, 1805*)

Stephen Jenks
(1772–1856)

3
Lord keep us safe this night,
Secure from all our fears;
May angels guard us while we sleep,
Till morning light appears.

5
And when our days are past,
And we from time remove;
O may we in thy bosom rest,
The bosom of thy love.

John Leland
(1754–1841)

62. SPRING

1800

Evangelical Harmony
Daniel Belknap
(*Boston, 1800*)

Daniel Belknap
(1771–1815)

63. SUMMER

1800

Evangelical Harmony
Daniel Belknap
(*Boston, 1800*)

Daniel Belknap
(1771–1815)

a - way! The spi - cy shrub, and flow'r with
head in - clin'd, Must per - ish leav - ing not a
wreck be - - hind! Thus the rich growth of the most friend - ly
clime, Must fall a vic - tim to de - vour - ing time.

64. AUTUMN

1800

Evangelical Harmony
Daniel Belknap
(*Boston, 1800*)

Daniel Belknap
(1771–1815)

na - ked and de - form'd are seen, The mea - dows late - ly
drest in green: The groves and fields are
dis - ar - ray'd, The song - sters of the wood are fled.

65. WINTER

1800

Evangelical Harmony
Daniel Belknap
(*Boston, 1800*)

Daniel Belknap
(1771–1815)

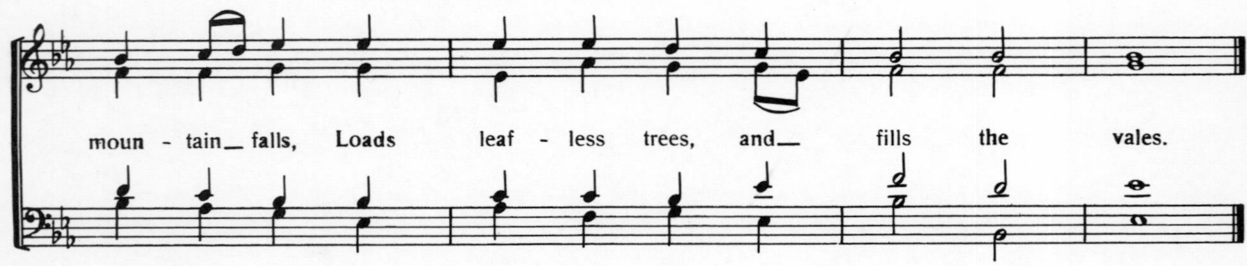

Note: The "Piano" and "Forte" are in the original.

66. ARNHEIM

1799

The Columbian Repository
Samuel Holyoke
(*Exeter, 1799*)

Samuel Holyoke
(1762–1820)

2

Sing, how he left the worlds of light,
And the bright robes he wore above;
How swift and joyful was his flight,
On wings of everlasting love.

7

Among a thousand harps and songs,
Jesus, the God, exalted reigns;
His sacred name fills all their tongues,
And echoes through the heav'nly plains!

Hymn: Isaac Watts (1707)
(1674–1748)

67. INNOCENT SOUNDS

1805

The Christian Harmony
Jeremiah Ingalls
(*Exeter, 1805*)

Jeremiah Ingalls
(1764–1828)

2

Who, on the part of God, will rise,
  Innocent sounds recover;
Fly on the prey, and seize the prize,
  Plunder the carnal lover:
Strip him of every moving strain,
  Of every melting measure;
Music in virtue's cause retain,
  Risk the holy pleasure.

5

Then let us in his praises join,
  Triumph in his salvation,
Glory ascribe to love divine,
  Worship and adoration.
Heaven already is begun,
  Open'd to each believer,
Only believe, and still sing on,
  Heaven is ours for ever.

68. NORTHFIELD

1798

The Christian Harmony
Jeremiah Ingalls
(*Exeter, 1805*)

Jeremiah Ingalls
(1764–1828)

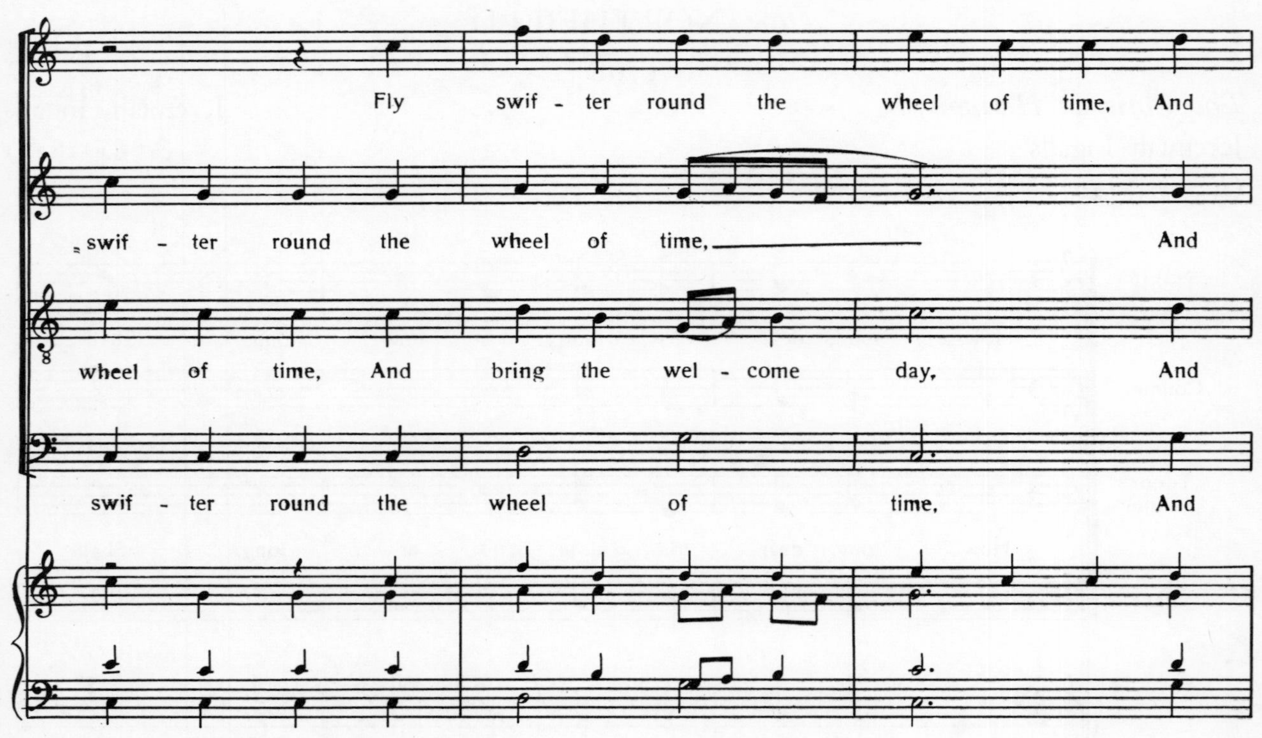
Fly swif - ter round the wheel of time, And
swif - ter round the wheel of time,
And
wheel of time, And bring the wel - come day,
And
swif - ter round the wheel of time,
And

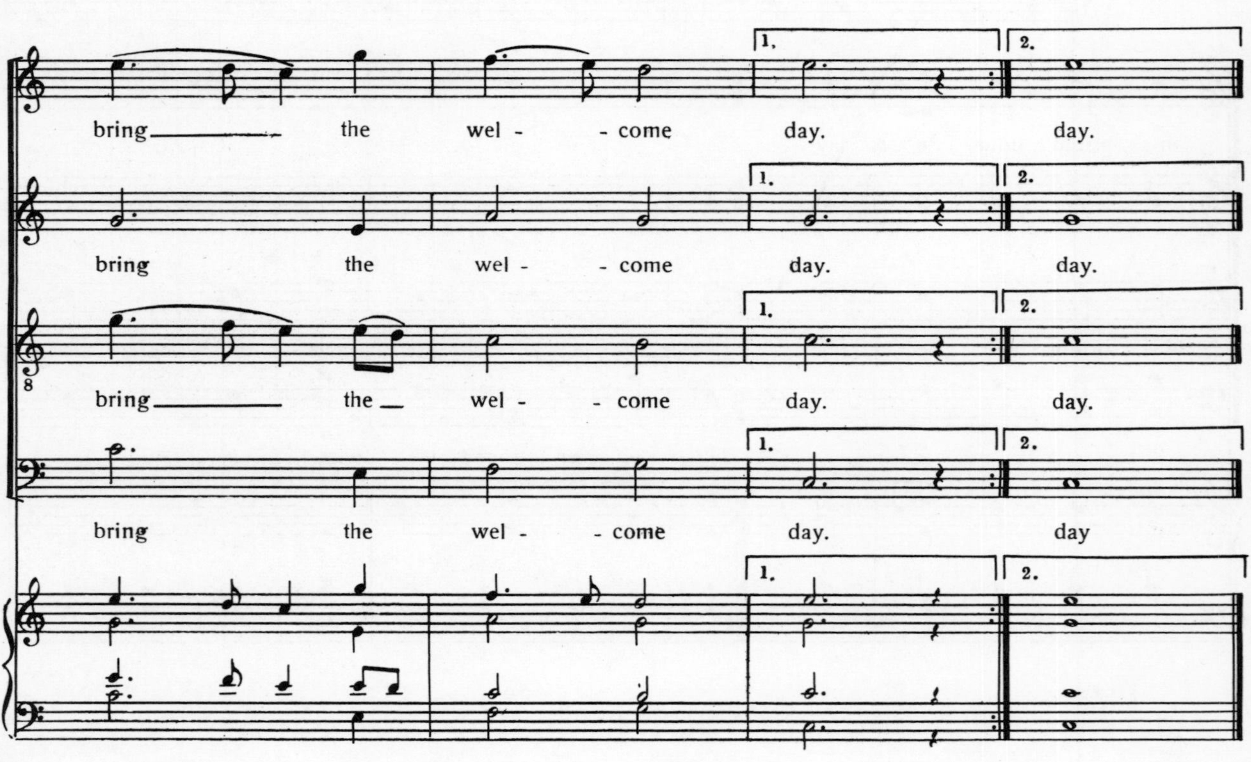
1.
2.
bring the wel - come day.
day.
bring the wel - come day.
day.
bring the wel - come day.
day.
bring the wel - come day.
day

69. THANKSGIVING ANTHEM

1809

Printed and sold by H. Mann, for the Author (*Dedham, 1809*)

Oliver Shaw (1779–1848)

f
Tell the people, what things — he hath done, — Tell the people,
Tell the people, what things — he hath done, — Tell the people,
Tell the people, what things he hath done, Tell the people,
Tell the people, what things — he hath done, Tell the people,
p

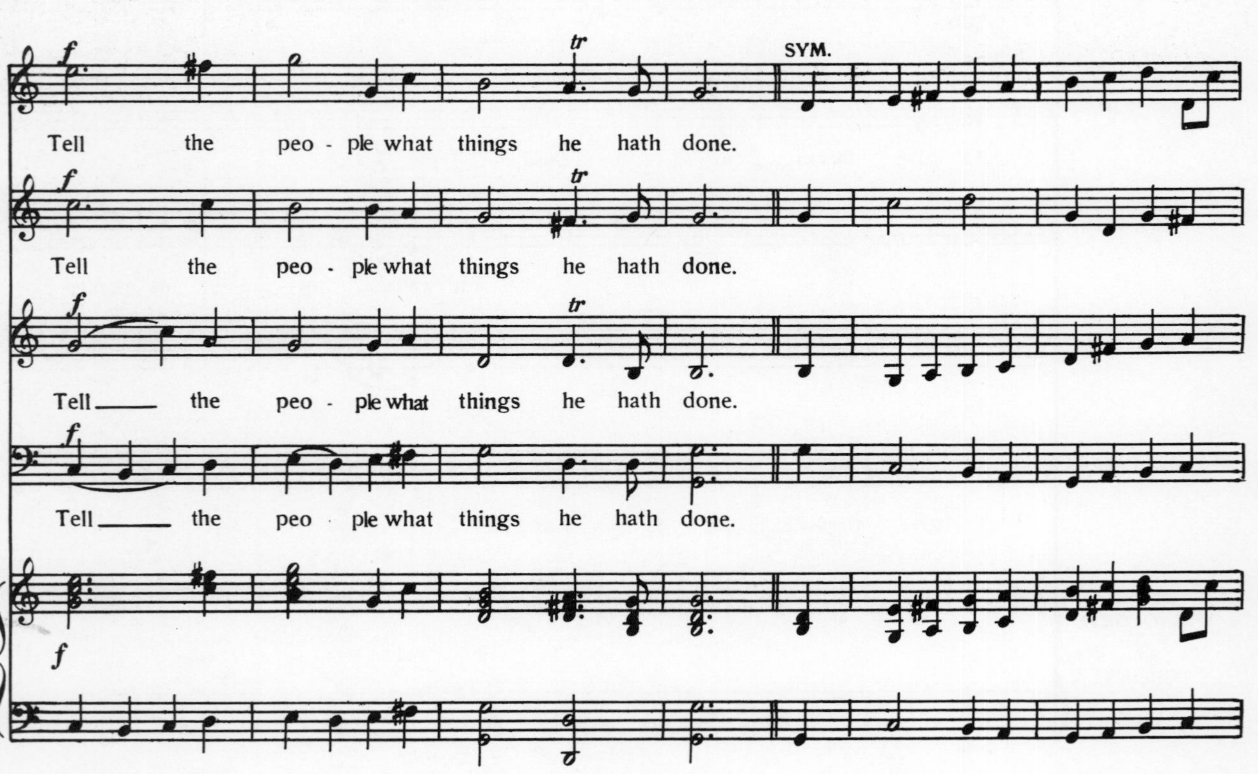
tr
SYM.
Tell the peo - ple what things he hath done.
Tell the peo - ple what things he hath done.
Tell — the peo - ple what things he hath done.
Tell — the peo - ple what things he hath done.
f

p
O let your songs be of him and praise him,
p
O let your songs be of him and praise him,
p

f
O let your songs be of him and praise him, And let your talk-ing
dolce
f
O let your songs be of him and praise him, And let your talk-ing
f
O let your songs be of him and praise him,
f
O let your songs be of him and praise him,
dolce
f

f
be of all his won'drous works, re - joice, re - joice in his ho - ly name, re -
be of all his won'drous works, re - joice, re - joice in his ho - ly name, re -
re - joice, re - joice in his ho - ly name, re -
re - joice, re - joice in his ho - ly name, re -

SYM.
tr
joice in his ho - ly name.
joice in his ho - ly name.
joice in his ho - ly name.
joice in his ho - ly name.

Allegretto
Let the heart_ of them_ re - joice that seek,_that seek,_ the Lord;
Let the heart of them_ re - joice that seek, that seek,_ the Lord;
Let the heart of them_ re - joice that seek, that seek,_ the Lord;
Let_ the heart of them_ re - joice that seek, that seek,_ the Lord;

SOLO
Seek_ the Lord_ and his_ strength,_ seek_ his face_ for - e - ver more.

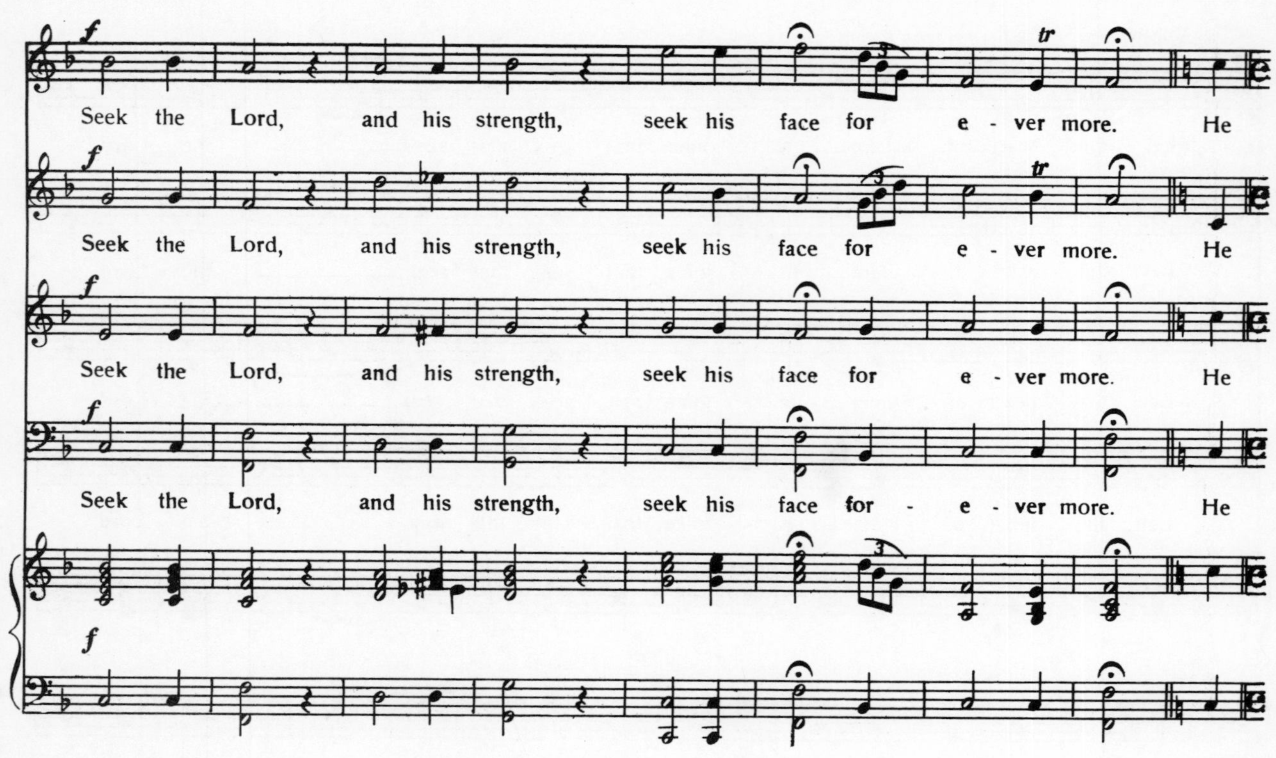
f
Seek the Lord, and his strength, seek his face for e - ver more. He
tr
Seek the Lord, and his strength, seek his face for e - ver more. He
Seek the Lord, and his strength, seek his face for e - ver more. He
Seek the Lord, and his strength, seek his face for - e - ver more. He

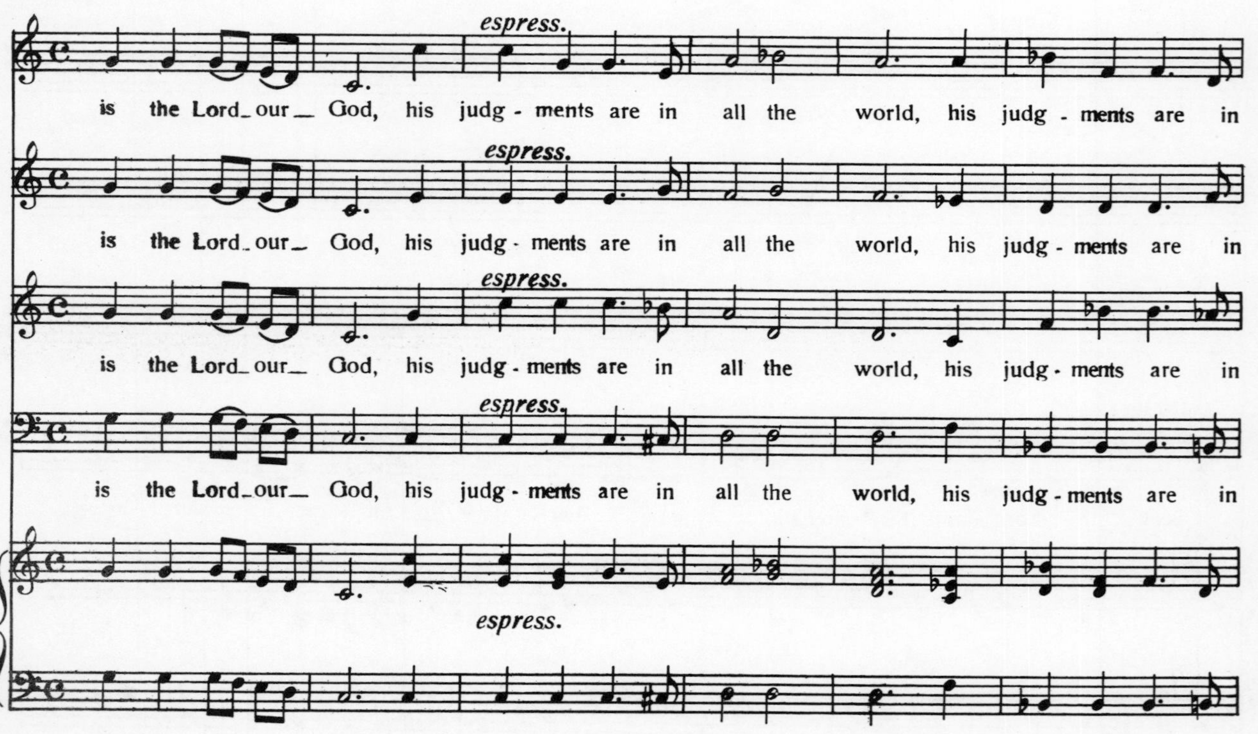
espress.
is the Lord_our_ God, his judg - ments are in all the world, his judg - ments are in
is the Lord_our_ God, his judg - ments are in all the world, his judg - ments are in
is the Lord_our_ God, his judg - ments are in all the world, his judg - ments are in
is the Lord_our_ God, his judg - ments are in all the world, his judg - ments are in

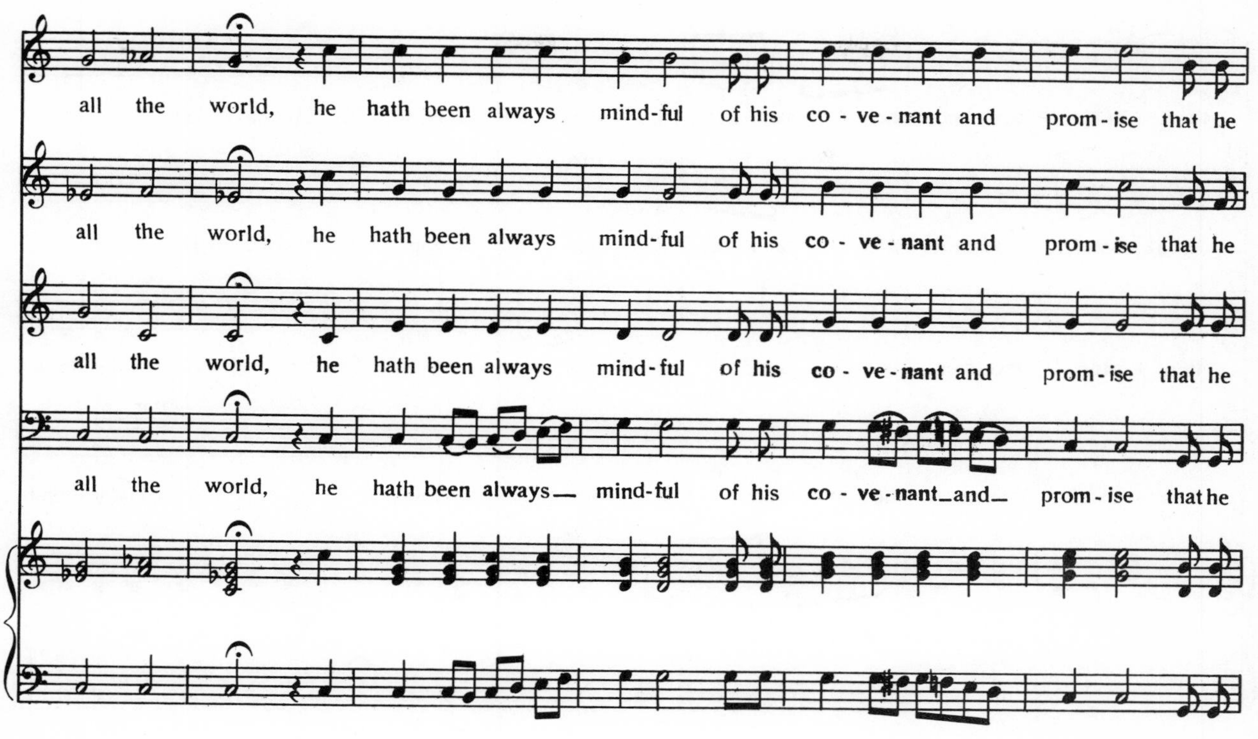
all the world, he hath been always mind-ful of his co - ve - nant and prom - ise that he
all the world, he hath been always mind-ful of his co - ve - nant and prom - ise that he
all the world, he hath been always mind-ful of his co - ve - nant and prom - ise that he
all the world, he hath been always— mind-ful of his co - ve - nant—and— prom - ise that he

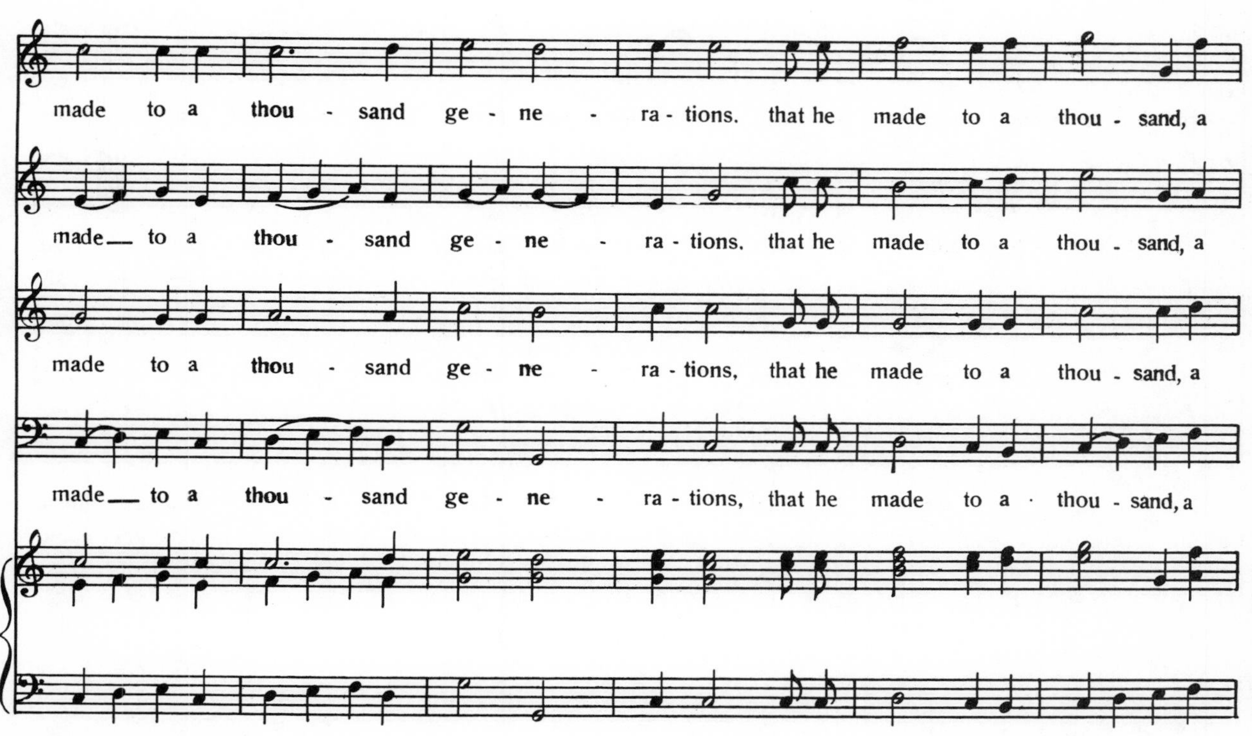
made to a thou - sand ge - ne - ra - tions. that he made to a thou - sand, a
made— to a thou - sand ge - ne - ra - tions, that he made to a thou - sand, a
made to a thou - sand ge - ne - ra - tions, that he made to a thou - sand, a
made— to a thou - sand ge - ne - ra - tions, that he made to a · thou - sand, a

tr
p
thou - sand, thou-sand, thou - sand ge - ne - ra-tions Hal-le-lu-jah.
thou - sand, thou-sand, thou - sand ge - ne - ra-tions Hal-le-lu jah.
thou - sand, thou-sand, thou - sand ge - ne - ra-tions Hal-le-lu-jah.
thou - sand, thou-sand, thou - sand ge - ne - ra-tions Hal-le-lu-jah.

f
p
Hal - le - lu - jah. A - men. Hal-le-lu-jah. Hal-le - lu - - jah. A - men.
Hal - le - lu - jah. A - men. Hal-le-lu-jah. Hal-le - lu - - jah. A - men.
Hal - le - lu - jah. A - men. Hal-le - lu - - jah. A - men.
Hal - le - lu - jah. A - men. Hal-le - lu - - jah. A - men.

Chapter Five

EUROPEAN MUSICIANS IN CHARLESTON, PHILADELPHIA, NEW YORK, AND BOSTON

Mr. and Mrs. Van Hagen, Messrs. Moller and Rausch, most respectfully solicit the patronage of their friends and the public, to Three Concerts, as follows, viz.

	Dols.	Cts.
A subscriber for a ticket to admit 2 ladies and a gentleman to the concerts, to pay	6	
Do. for do. one lady and a gentleman	4	50
Do. for do. one person	3	
Non-subscribers for each concert	1	25

After each Concert, a Ball

Advertisement in *The Daily Advertiser* New York, Thursday, December 24, 1795

During the pre-Revolutionary period, professionally trained European musicians, in addition to those in the religious communities, began to arrive in America to seek their fortune. Charleston, South Carolina was the main center of attraction at first, but after the Revolution many settled in Philadelphia, New York, and Boston.

Public concerts were held in Boston and Charleston as early as 1731 and 1732.[1] Charles-

[1] O. G. Sonneck, *Early Concert Life in America (1731–1800)*, Leipzig: Breitkopf & Härtel, 1907.

ton saw the first performance of a ballad opera in 1735, and the St. Cecilia Society was formed there in 1762. Williamsburg was dominated by the British, and the inhabitants "behaved themselves exactly as the Gentry in London."

In 1736 the first concert in New York was given as a benefit for Charles Theodore Pachelbel (Pachelbell) before his departure for Charleston. Pachelbel, a son of the famous German organist Johann Pachelbel, arrived in Boston about 1732 and was one of the first of the European musicians who were to come to America in large numbers after the Revolutionary War. These musicians carried on their activities as composers, performers, conductors, impresarios, teachers, publishers, and sellers of music and musical instruments, and they virtually took over the musical life from Virginia to Massachusetts.

The self-taught, native-born composers of late 18th-century New England were soon totally eclipsed, and their music was replaced by that of Handel, Haydn, Stamitz, and their professional rivals from Europe. The New England composers had concentrated their efforts on psalm-tunes, fuging tunes, hymns, set pieces, and anthems, mostly with religious texts, while the foreign-born professionals were particularly interested in music for public entertainment—compositions for keyboard, small instrumental groups, ballad operas, and secular songs. Oscar Sonneck's *Bibliography of Early Secular American Music of the 18th Century*, revised by William Treat Upton in 1945, lists over 3500 items. Most of this music was by foreign composers, and it was published principally between 1790 and 1800. Among the more influential musicians who came to America in pre-Revolutionary days, in addition to Pachelbel, were William Tuckey, Peter A. van Hagen, Sr., Jacob Eckhard, and William Selby.

William Tuckey, one of the early arrivals from England, came to New York in 1753. Simeon Jocelin might have had Tuckey's *Knighton* (No. 70) in mind when he stated in the Preface to his *Chorister's Companion* (1782) that "the tunes formerly in common use are now laid aside, instead of which those of a more lively and airy tune are substituted."

One of Charleston's leading musicians from 1786 until his death in 1833 was the German composer Jacob Eckhard, who first settled in Richmond in 1776. *The Pillar of Glory*, for solo voice and unison chorus (No. 71), was written to celebrate the American victories at sea over Albion (England) in the War of 1812. Eckhard, whose acquaintance with *To Anacreon in Heaven* is obvious, "gained a prize" for his piece in a national competition held in 1813.

William Selby, a London organist and composer, settled in Boston in 1771 and for many years played an active part in the development of the musical life there. His *Voluntary VIII* (No. 72) was written so that it could be played on the organ or harpsichord, a characteristic of much keyboard music of the period. The short prelude in Handelian style is unified by a recurring 32nd-note figure and comes to an unusual cadence on C-sharp. The free fugue that follows returns to the original key of A major. Alberti-bass figures (in the upper part also) and long episodes of sequences are characteristic of this music. Selby's *Ode for the New Year* (No. 73) is for two solo voices in simple duple time with a three-part chorus in compound duple time. This fine composition was written as a tribute to George Washington, who was then, 1790, beginning his second year as President of the United States.

Following the Revolutionary War, Philadelphia replaced Charleston as a musical center, and the English musicians Alexander Reinagle, Raynor Taylor, and Benjamin Carr were active there for many years.

Reinagle's Sonata in E major, composed after 1786, is the second of four sonatas he wrote for the pianoforte. The *Anthology* includes the second and third movements of this three-movement work (No. 74), taken from the original manuscript. In binary form, the Adagio opens in E minor with an eight-measure introduction followed by the principal theme, the lyricism of which bears a close affinity to the style of Carl Philipp Emanuel

Bach's sonatas. The subordinate theme in G major (measure 17) brings the first part to a close at the double bar. The second part, in G major, presents the theme in a highly embellished form. This culminates in a short cadenza, followed by the return of the principal theme in its original key (m. 53). Marked Allegro, the gay third movement is in a modified second rondo form with a coda. A short cadenza precedes the final appearance of the first theme.

The title of Raynor Taylor's *Sonata for the Piano Forte with an Accompaniment for A Violin* would seem to imply a subordinate role for the violin, but a glance at the score shows that the violin is not treated as an *ad libitum* instrument and that both instruments are about equally active, even though the violin part is contained within the first position. The accompanied sonata represents an important stage in the transition from the Baroque solo sonata with continuo accompaniment to the Classic sonata for piano and violin. The present Sonata (No. 75) is in two movements; the first, marked Andante, is in binary form with the first section repeated, and the second is a Tempo di Menuetto with the usual Minuet–Trio–Minuet (varied).

Benjamin Carr, one of the most influential foreign musicians of his time in this country, wrote the music for the ballad opera *The Archers; or, the Mountaineers of Switzerland.* The opera, adapted by William Dunlap from the story of William Tell, was first performed by the Old American Company of New York on April 18, 1796. The song *Why, Huntress, why?* (No. 76) was published in Carr's *Musical Journal*, and it is one of the two numbers from the opera that have survived.

Among the prominent foreign-born musicians in New York during the post-Revolutionary period were the Englishman James Hewitt (an exact contemporary of Beethoven), the Frenchman Victor Pelissier, and John Christopher Moller, who came from England.

Alknomook (No. 77), subtitled *The Death Song of the Cherokee Indians*, is the sole surviving excerpt from the ballad opera *Tammany*, by James Hewitt. It is a musical trifle but is included here because *Tammany* is perhaps the first ballad opera composed in the United States and because of its political connotation. The opera takes its name from the Tammany Society, founded by William Mooney in New York in 1789, who called it Tammany in honor of a Cherokee chieftain. Produced in 1794 under the auspices of the Tammany Society, the opera deals with the struggle against the aristocratic theories of the Anti-Federalists by allegorically portraying the stoicism of the Cherokees. Tammany laments the fate of his tribe in this short strophic air, completely devoid of Indian flavor, which Hewitt borrowed for inclusion in his work. The tune enjoyed wide favor in Scotland, England, and the Colonies, and it eventually found its way into Southern folk hymnody (compare with *Morality*, No. 92).

Few are the joys (No. 78) is one of two surviving pieces from Pelissier's ballad opera *Edwin and Angelina*, whose libretto was adapted from a novel by Oliver Goldsmith. The French composer presented his opera in New York in December of 1796 with marked success.

John C. Moller's *Sinfonia* (No. 79), of which only the piano reduction has survived, was printed and sold by Moller and Capron in 1793. An unusual feature of this composition is the second movement, a Menuetto with an interpolated Rondo having the form: minuet –rondo–minuet.

European musicians had taken an increasingly active part in the musical life of Boston from the time of William Selby's arrival in 1771. Among those who settled there after the Revolution were Hans Gram from Denmark, Peter A. van Hagen, Sr. and his musical family from Holland, and the Englishman George K. Jackson.

Gram, although an influential composer of anthems, is known today principally through his solo song *The Death Song of an Indian Chief* (1791, No. 80). This song is accompanied by a small ensemble and is the first orchestral score to be published in the United States. The title page reads:

The Death Song of an Indian Chief. Taken from OUABI, an Indian Tale, in Four Cantos, by PHILENIA, a Lady of Boston. Set to Musick by Mr. Hans Gram, of Boston.

Many songs and poems were written in honor of George Washington while he was alive. Following his death in 1799, an unparaleled number of "sacred dirges" were published of which Peter van Hagen's simple, through-composed song (No. 81) is typical.

George K. Jackson was one of the more able musicians who came to America just before the turn of the century. His *Verses for the Fourth of July* (No. 82) is a festive piece composed during his residence in New York and before he settled in Boston in 1812. Only the keyboard score, with some instruments cued in, has survived. The anthem is for solo voice and chorus, with a violin part that occasionally doubles the vocal line. The title page states that the composition was sung at the Presbyterian Church in New York. Jackson exerted a considerable influence on American composers of the next generation, particularly through his association with the Handel and Haydn Society and Lowell Mason.

70. KNIGHTON

1782

The Chorister's Companion
Simeon Jocelin
(*New Haven, 1782*)

William Tuckey
(1708–1781)

Ps. 108: Nahum Tate
(1652–1715)

71. NAVAL SONG

The Pillar of Glory

1813

Edwin C. Holland

Jacob Eckhard, Sr.
(1757–1833)

[1] F-sharp in the original.

4

Already the storm of contention has hurl'd,
From the grasp of Old England the TRIDENT of WAR,
The beams of our STARS have illumin'd the world,
Unfurl'd our Standard beats proud in the air:
Wild glares the Eagle's eye,
Swift as he cuts the sky,
Marking the wake where our heroes advance;
Compass'd with rays of light,
Hovers he o'er the fight;
Albion is heartless—and stoops to his glance.

72. VOLUNTARY VIII

c. 1767

Ten Voluntarys for the Organ or Harpsichord (London, c. 1767)

William Selby (1738–1798)

tr
tr

73. ODE FOR THE NEW YEAR

January 1, 1790

The Massachusetts Magazine (*Boston, 1789*)

William Selby (1738–1798)

Treble

Bass

Hark! notes me - lo - dious fill the skies! "From

The - tis' lap, A - pol - lo rise! Thy swift wheel'd cha-riot speed, Thy

swift wheel'd cha - riot speed a - main! O'er fleet - ing cour - sers,

2

"And as the golden car of light,
Refulgent beams on mortal sight;
As fiery steeds (which oft times lave
Their winged feet in ocean's wave)
Ascend above the mantling deep,
And rapid gain th' empyrean steep,
Let slumb'ring nations rise, and loud pro-long,
To Day's celestial Prince, the choral song."

3

Columbia heard the high behest,
Her free born millions smote the breast!
And silent slept the heav'n strung lyre,
Till Freedom breath'd impassion'd fire;
Till Virtue form'd the hallow'd sound,
And Fame enraptur'd roll'd it round.
"All hail to Freedom's, Virtue's, Glory's Sun!
Ye worlds repeat, repeat! 'Tis WASHINGTON"!

74. SONATA IN E FOR THE PIANO FORTE

Adagio—Allegro

From the original manuscript

Alexander Reinagle (1756–1809)

[1] The two dots indicate a sharp.

tr
R
L
p
f
tr
p
f
tr
f
tr
f
p

f
p
3
3
3
3
tr
tr
f
f

rinf.
cresc.
f
p
rinf.

tr
R
p
f
p
f
tr
tr
tr
f

Allegro
cresc.
f
tr
tr

tr
f
p
tr
tr
p
tr
f

p
f
p
f
f
f
p
tr
tr
f

Cadenza
adagio
tr
p
f
p
f

Tempo Primo
tr
tr

75. SONATA FOR THE PIANO FORTE WITH AN ACCOMPANIMENT FOR A VIOLIN

1797

Carr's Musical Repository
(*Philadelphia*, 1797)

Raynor Taylor
(1747–1825)

tr
mf
f
p

tr
mf
f
6
3
ff
8ths

tr
mf
p
f

mf
tr
f
tr
tr
mf
f
tr
mf
tr

f
p
mf
tr
f
mf
ff
mf
ff

Tempo di Menuetto
tr
mf
p
f

76. WHY, HUNTRESS, WHY?

from
The Archers

1796

William Dunlap

Benjamin Carr
(1768–1831)

Ah! think what pangs thy Father still must feel,
What pangs must Arnold know,
When thou'rt expos'd unto the biting steel
Shall rush amid the foe,
Then, Huntress, why wilt thou thy life expose?

77. ALKNOMOOK

The Death Song of the Cherokee Indians
from
Tammany

1794

Ann Julia Hatton

James Hewitt (1770–1827)

2

Remember the Arrows he shot from his Bow,
Remember your Chiefs by his Hatchet laid low,
Why so slow, do you wait 'till I shrink from the pain,
No, the Son of ALKNOMOOK Will never complain.

3

Remember the wood where in Ambush we lay,
And the Scalps which we bore from your Nation away,
Now the flame rises fast, you Exult in my pain,
But the Son of ALKNOMOOK can never complain.

4

I go to the Land where my Father is gone,
His Ghost shall rejoice in that of his Son;
Death comes like a friend, he relieves me from pain,
And thy Son O! ALKNOMOOK has scorn'd to complain.

78. FEW ARE THE JOYS

from
Edwin and Angelina

1797

Elihu Hubbard Smith

Victor Pelissier

ten - dent on a love sin - cere, I'll try my Free - - dom
to re - gain how - e - 'er the task may prove se -
vere how - e'er the task may
prove se - - vere may prove se - - vere.
p

Yes, hear me Cu - pid
I re - solve hence-forth to treat thee
as a foe no more this heart thou

shalt — in - volve — in anx - ious Jal - - ous -

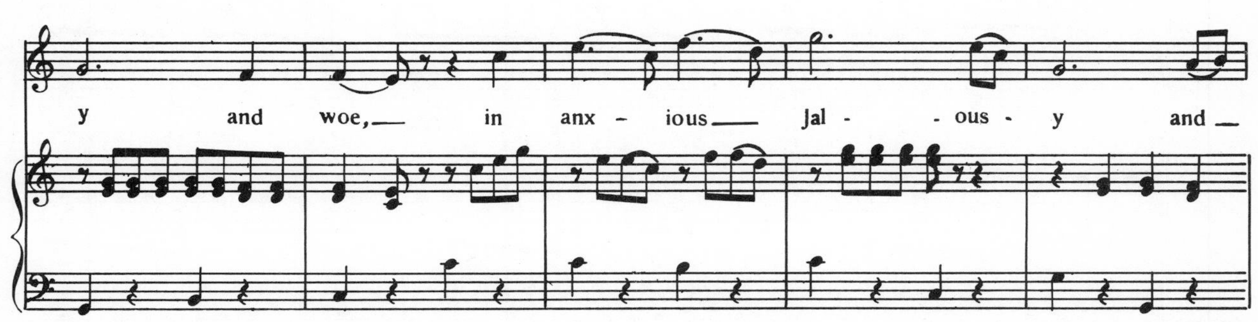
y and woe, — in anx – ious — Jal - - ous - y and —

woe.

pp
pp

79. SINFONIA

1793

Moller and Capron's Monthly Numbers
The First Number, 1793

John Christopher Moller
(d. 1803)

Menuetto
ff
p
Grazioso
f p
f p
f (p)
tr
fp
fp
tr
tr

Rondo Allegro
p
p
ff
Oboe Solo

Menuet
ff
ff

80. THE DEATH SONG OF AN INDIAN CHIEF

1791

By Philenia, a Lady of Boston
[Sarah Wentworth Morton]

Hans Gram

tenuto
tr
Rear'd — midst the war-em-pur-pled plain, What Il - li - nois sub - mits to pain! How
tenuto
tenuto
tenuto
poco f
can the glo-ry - dart - ing fire, The cow- ard chill of death — in - spire, — The

[1] The first two eighth notes are A-flat in the original.

80a. THE DEATH SONG OF AN INDIAN CHIEF

1791

By Philenia, a Lady of Boston
[Sarah Wentworth Morton]

Hans Gram
Arranged from the full score

tenuto
plain, What Il - li - nois sub - mits to pain! How
shine, And own their FLAM - ING SOURCE di - vine. Then
fear, Not all your force can start a tear. Think
tenuto
can the glo - ry - dart - - ing fire, The cow - ard chill of
let me hail th' IM - MOR - - TAL FIRE, And in the sa - cred
not with me my tribe de - cays, More glo - rious chiefs the
f
death in - spire, The cow - ard chill of death in -
flames ex - pire; Nor yet those Hu - ron hands re -
hatch - - et raise; Not un - re - veng'd their sa - - chem
mf
spire, The cow - ard chill of death in - spire!
strain; This bo - som scorns the throbs of pain.
dies, Not un - at - tend - ed greets the skies.
p
dim.

81. FUNERAL DIRGE ON THE DEATH OF GENERAL WASHINGTON

1799

Peter A. van Hagen, Sr.
(1750–1803)

Grave

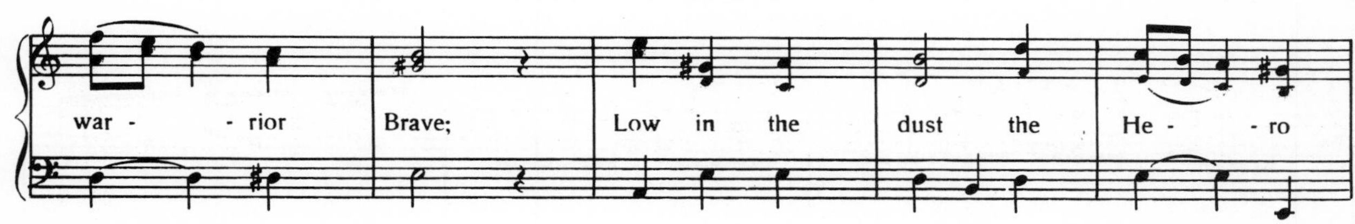

2

By thee inspir'd with warlike art
He urg'd the fight, or bade it cease:
Not less he fill'd the statesman's part:
Our guide in war, our head in Peace.

3

His Country happy, great, and free,
Hail'd him her Father, hope, and pride:
But fix'd, O God, his hope on thee,
He liv'd thy friend, thy servant died.

82. VERSES FOR THE FOURTH OF JULY

1801

Mrs. George K. Jackson

George K. Jackson (1745–1823)

When gen-'rous Free-dom leaves her dow-ny
bed, And Proud Be-lo-na droops her Aw-ful
head. Then more than Hap-pi-ness with wide do-
main Ex-tends to ev-'ry Maid and Vil-lage
dolce
dolce
tr
tr

Swain, Extends to ev-'ry Maid and Village
Chorus
Swain While Guardian Angels waving in the
Air, Fair Freedom's Banners
high up-lift-ed bear, Fair Free-dom's— Ban-ners high up - lift - ed

2

The lovely Cherub Contemplation bring,
Let Harmony soft Hymeneals sing
Of gentle Love, and his fantastic toys,
Of Health, Domestic Peace, and all their Joys;
Chorus: While Guardian Angels etc.

3

Their Trumpets, sounding Fame, in Concert hear
Of Washington, Great Washington revere.
Him first, him best, our grateful hours employ
The Great, the Good, and Source of all your Joy.
Chorus: While Guardian Angels etc.

Chapter Six

LOWELL MASON AND HIS CONTEMPORARIES

"The chief value of music . . . in schools or families, will be social and moral."

Lowell Mason

CHURCH and school music and music education were dominated by Lowell Mason (1792–1872) and his contemporaries for at least sixty years of the 19th century. Mason's chief contribution to music in America was the introduction of singing classes in the public schools and the establishment of teacher-training institutes. The singing schools of the early 19th century provided the first teachers and "methods" for this new development. Mason also organized "musical conventions" in various parts of the country and was influential in the establishment of theoretical and practical music in many of the new liberal arts colleges in the Midwest.

These activities required music, and Mason and his co-workers published a large number of collections, which included psalm-tunes, hymns, chants, sentences, motets, and anthems. Tunes from the works of European composers were freely arranged and harmonized by Mason, Hastings, Webb, Bradbury, Woodbury, and others, who also contributed hymns and some anthems of their own. A few tunes by the earlier English composers, such as Tans'ur, Playford, Williams, and the Americans Read, Holden, and others, were retained to satisfy the "old-fashioned" tastes.

It was Mason's desire to bring "music to the masses" and, as he said, to "reform" the church music of the 18th-century singing schools. He did reach the masses through his manifold activities; and the many tunebooks, which always included some of his music and that of his associates, had a wide circulation through the East and Midwest, bringing him both fame and fortune. The psalm-tunes and fuging tunes of his New England predecessors were mostly eliminated in favor of a standard type of "better music" with simple, melodious harmonies which represented "scientific progress."

The hymns of Mason and his contemporaries were probably suited to the needs of their time and represented an improvement over many of the cheap, secular revival songs in current use. However, the sentimental texts and lack of distinction and originality in the music did little to elevate musical taste. Many of their hymns, although appearing less and less frequently in modern hymnals, still have a firm hold on Protestant congregations today.

Typical hymns, included in the *Anthology* in their original version, are Mason's *From Greenland's icy mountains* (*A Missionary Hymn*, No. 83) and *My faith looks up to Thee* (*Olivet*, No. 84), Hastings's *Rock of Ages* (*Toplady*, No. 86), and Bradbury's *Woodworth* (No. 88), best known today with the text "Just as I am, without one plea."

From Greenland's icy mountains was originally composed and published as a solo song and dedicated to Miss Mary W. Howard of Savannah, Georgia. The song was later included in Mason's publications as a three-part, and subsequently as a four-part, hymn.

Mason set a new text to Aaron Williams's tune, *St. Thomas's* (*Anthology*, No. 29), and moved the melody from the tenor to the treble voice (No. 85). He also added a typical "Hallelujah" coda and a figured bass for the organ, an innovation of his that is found for the first time in American tunebooks.

The well-known tune by George Webb is given in its original form as a secular song, *'Tis dawn, the lark is singing* (No. 87). Samuel Francis Smith, the author of "My country, 'tis of thee," set his text "The morning light is breaking" to the tune in 1832; and in 1859 George Duffield, Jr. used the tune for his text beginning "Stand up, stand up for Jesus." Webb introduced an unusual and practical way of making a keyboard score for the organist by adding the alto and tenor parts in small notes to the treble and bass parts.

One of the comparatively few collections of secular music of this period was Isaac B. Woodbury's *Song Crown*, a collection of glees, quartets, opera choruses, trios, solos, and miscellaneous pieces. His two glees, *The Farmer's Daughter* (No. 89) and *Stars of the Summer Night* (No. 90), were the outgrowth of his travels with the Bay State Glee Club, which he conducted, and the latter glee is found in many college song books today.

83. FROM GREENLAND'S ICY MOUNTAINS

A Missionary Hymn

1824

Published by G. Willig, Jr.
(*Baltimore, 1824*)

Lowell Mason
(1792–1872)

2

What tho' the spicy breezes blow soft o'er Ceylon's isle;
Tho' ev'ry prospect pleases and only man is vile;
In vain with lavish kindness the gifts of God are strown;
The heathen in his blindness bows down to wood and stone.

3

Shall we, whose souls are lighted by wisdom from on high,
Shall we to men benighted the lamp of life deny?
Salvation! O Salvation! the joyful sound proclaim,
Till earth's remotest nation has learnt Messiah's name.

4

Waft, waft, ye winds, his story, and you, ye waters, roll,
Till like a sea of glory it spreads from pole to pole;
Till o'er our ransom'd nature the Lamb for sinners slain,
Redeemer, King, Creator, returns in bliss to reign.

Bishop Reginald Heber (1819)
(1783–1826)

84. MY FAITH LOOKS UP TO THEE

(Olivet)

1831

Spiritual Songs for Social Worship
Lowell Mason and Thomas Hastings
(Utica, 1831)

Lowell Mason
(1792–1872)

Note: The spelling "Base" instead of "Bass" is often found in music of this period.

2

May thy rich grace impart
Strength to my fainting heart,
My zeal inspire;
As thou hast died for me,
Oh may my love to thee,
Pure, warm, and changeless be,
A burning fire.

3

While life's dark maze I tread,
And griefs around me spread,
Be thou my guide;
Bid darkness turn to day,
Wipe sorrow's tears away,
Nor let me ever stray,
From thee aside.

Ray Palmer (1830)
(1808–1887)

85. ST. THOMAS

1852

New Carmina Sacra
Lowell Mason
(*Boston, 1852*)

Aaron Williams
(1731–1776)
Arranged by Lowell Mason
(1792–1872)

Note: The tenors may sing the first three notes of the second phrase in thirds. The pedal point should be played on the organ or a bass instrument. The "Hallelujahs" (added by Lowell Mason) were not only to be used at the close of the hymn, but could be introduced before the first stanza and between the stanzas.

2

His pow'r subdues our sins;
And his forgiving love,
Far as the east is from the west,
Doth all our guilt remove.

4

High as the heav'ns are rais'd
Above the ground we tread,
So far the riches of his grace
Our highest thoughts exceed.

Ps. 103: Isaac Watts (1719)
(1674–1748)

86. ROCK OF AGES

(Toplady)

1831

Spiritual Songs for Social Worship
Lowell Mason and Thomas Hastings
(Utica, 1831)

Thomas Hastings
(1784–1872)

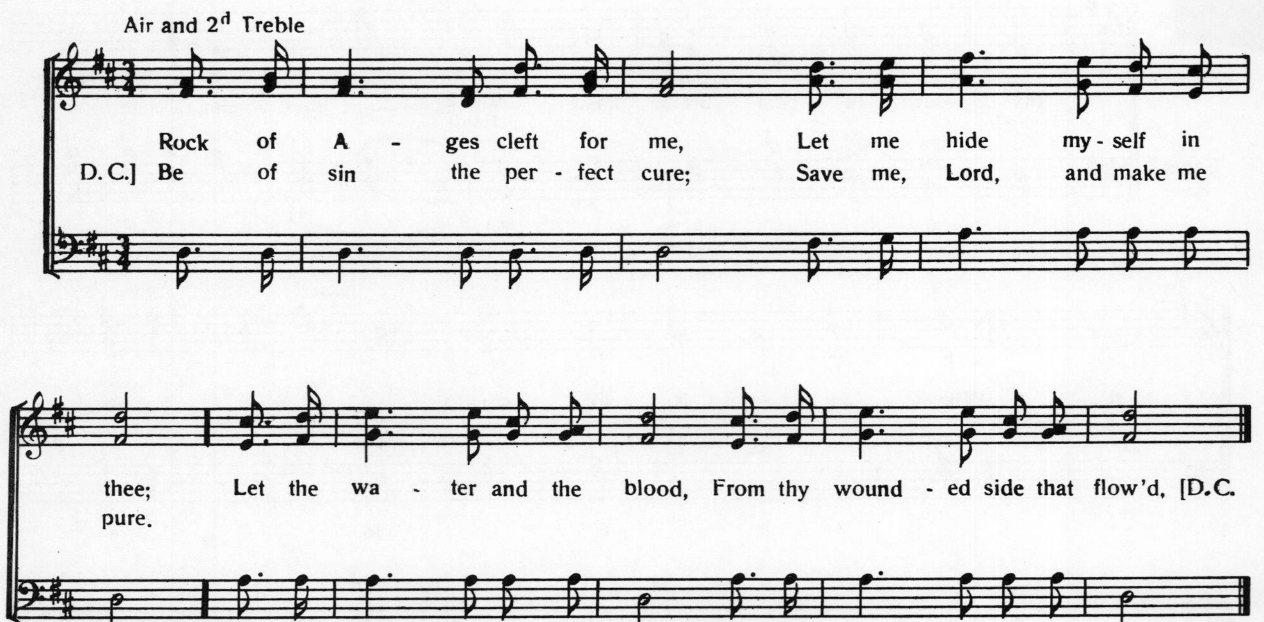

2

Should my tears for ever flow;
Should my zeal no languor know;
This for sin could not atone:
Thou must save, and thou alone.
In my hand no price I bring;
Simply to thy cross I cling.

3

While I draw this fleeting breath,
When mine eyelids close in death,
When I rise to worlds unknown,
And behold thee on thy throne,
Rock of Ages, cleft for me,
Let me hide myself in thee.

Augustus M. Toplady (1776)
(1740–1778)

87. 'TIS DAWN, THE LARK IS SINGING

1837

[...]e Odeon
[...]orge J. Webb
([...]ston, 1837)

George J. Webb
(1803–1887)

2

The birds, they seem to send,
Their sweetest notes on high,
For benefits that blend
Their being with the sky.
And Oh, may I bestow,
My first, last, thought on heaven;
And may my bosom glow
With thanks each morn and even!

88. WOODWORTH

1849

The Mendelssohn Collection
William Bradbury and Thomas Hastings
(*New York, 1849*)

William B. Bradbury
(1816–1868)

Soft and gentle, but not too slow

[1] The first note in the alto is B in later editions.

2

Yet not one murmuring wish or thought
Should with our mourning passion blend;
Nor should our bleeding hearts forget
Th'almighty, ever-living Friend.

89. THE FARMER'S DAUGHTER

1856

The Song Crown
Isaac B. Woodbury
(*New York, 1856*)

Isaac B. Woodbury
(1819–1858)

90. STARS OF THE SUMMER NIGHT

1856

The Song Crown
Isaac B. Woodbury
(*New York, 1856*)

Isaac B. Woodbury
(1819–1858)

Henry Wadsworth Longfellow
(1807–1882)

Chapter Seven

SOUTHERN FOLK HYMNS

The watchmen blow the trumpet round,
Come listen to the solemn sound,
And be assured there's danger nigh,
How many are prepared to die?
Your days on earth will soon be o'er,
And time to you return no more;
O think thou hast a soul to save;
What are thy hopes beyond the grave?

William Walker, "The Watchman's Call" (*Southern Harmony*, 1835)

THE 18TH-CENTURY revival movement in America, which originated among the dissension groups of various denominations, began its development, especially among the Baptists in Massachusetts, with the "Great Awakening" under Jonathan Edwards and George Whitefield. The psalm-tunes of the early 18th-century Puritans no longer satisfied the revivalists who were "wont to sing with unusual elevation of heart and voice." A number of collections of English vocal music appeared in the second half of the century, and during the last two decades of the century the New England group of composers—Edson, Read, French, and others—wrote many tunes which had the characteristics of folk music.

The true folk hymn is based on a secular folk tune and is sung to a religious text. Only a few of these folk hymns, among them the well-known *Kedron* (No. 95), appeared in Northern collections before the close of the 18th century. Soon, however, tunebooks were published which included many folk hymns and these, as well as the psalm-tunes and fuging tunes of the New England composers, found their way into Southern collections.

The Kentucky Revival of 1800 led to the rapid development of folk hymnody in the South and the publication about 1815 of the first Southern tunebook, *Kentucky Harmony* by Ananias Davisson. This collection was followed by many other tunebooks, among them *The Missouri Harmony* (1820) by Allen D. Carden, *The Southern Harmony* (1835) by William Walker, and *The Sacred Harp* (1844) by B. F. White and E. J. King. These collections went through many editions and the music is still being used in "all-day sings" in rural communities. Irving Lowens [1] has pointed out that John Wyeth's *Repository of Sacred Music, Part Second* (1813) was an important source for the *Kentucky Harmony*. Three of the folk hymns that were originally found in Wyeth's *Repository, Part Second* (*Fairton*, No. 91; *Consolation*, No. 93; and *Primrose*, No. 94) are printed in this chapter of the *Anthology*.

The texts (many by Isaac Watts) of the Southern folk hymns were often adapted to fiddle tunes, ballads, and other secular sources from here and the British Isles. There are also many anonymous tunes and tunes ascribed to men about whom little or nothing is known.[2]

Southern collections of folk hymns are written in "shape-notes," sometimes called "buckwheat" or "patent" notes. The four-shape notation, introduced by William Little and William Smith in *The Easy Instructor* (Philadelphia, 1801), was used in the early tune-books; and later an effort was made to introduce a seven-shape system. The shape-notes are used with a conventional clef and key signature on lines and spaces and can be read as modern notation. The usual time signatures are found and also occasional instances of the use of the inverted C for $\frac{2}{2}$ time. The four shapes for the notes are right triangle (fa), used for the first and fourth degrees of the scale; round (sol), for the second and fifth degrees; square (la), for the third and sixth degrees; and diamond (mi), for the seventh degree.

Printed in score, the music is in three or four parts, with the tune customarily in the tenor. Later collections, notably the Denson Revision of *The Sacred Harp*, often have an alto part that was added to original three-part music. The collections also usually contained "grounds and rudiments of music" borrowed from various sources, including William Tans'ur.

The music was sung without accompaniment, and it was customary for all parts except the bass to be sung by both men and women. In four-part songs this resulted in the upper three parts being doubled at the octave, and, as Billings might have said, a tune so sung (although it has but four parts) is in effect the same as *seven*.

The singers received their tonic pitch from the leader of the group, first singing the song with the syllables represented by the shape-notes, and then with the text. When two notes occurred in one part ("choosing notes"), it was customary to sing both parts, although in some contexts one or the other note might be chosen. The tune in the tenor was often freely ornamented, the singer adding a higher or lower grace note before singing the mēlody note. Frequent use of slides, scoops, and anticipations is a characteristic performance practice, and only rarely do the ornamentations appear in the printed music.[3] The "coloring" of the intervals by the singers sometimes resulted in the singing of "neutral thirds."

A large majority of the tunes are modal or quasi-modal.[4] The Aeolian (natural minor) is frequently found (*Fairton; Consolation; Kedron* in *Southern Harmony*—No. 95a). *The Converted Thief* (No. 96) is in the Mixolydian mode, and *The Hebrew Children* (No. 97) is in the rarely used Phrygian mode. *Wondrous Love* (No. 101) is usually sung with a lowered sixth which places the tune in the Dorian mode. Melodies in the Ionian (major) mode include *Morality* (No. 92), *Primrose, Plenary* (No. 99), and *Gospel Trumpet* (No. 103). *Shouting Song* (No. 102) appears to be in F-sharp minor. The seventh is omitted, however, which leaves the tune with an ambiguous tonality.

Gapped melodies, with one or two scale

[1] Irving Lowens, "John Wyeth's *Repository of Sacred Music, Part Second*," *Journal of the American Musicological Society* V (1952), 114-131.

[2] The books by Dr. George Pullen Jackson should be consulted for a complete history of the Southern folk hymn.

[3] An ornamented version of *Amazing Grace* has been printed in Dr. Jackson's *Spiritual Folk-Songs of Early America* and quoted in *America's Music* by Gilbert Chase (New York, 1955), p. 203.

[4] The reader should remember that it is the tune that is being discussed, not the harmonization.

degrees omitted, are frequently used. The tunes in nine of the thirteen folk hymns printed in the *Anthology* have scale degrees omitted. Pentatonic melodies with the fourth and seventh omitted are found in *The Good Old Way* (No. 98), *Plenary* (No. 99), and *New Britain* (No. 100). The seventh is omitted in *Primrose*, the second in *The Hebrew Children*, the third in *The Converted Thief*, and the sixth in *Gospel Trumpet.*

Dyadic and triadic harmony and second-inversion chords are freely used with open and parallel fifths and octaves (*Fairton*, *Morality*, *Wondrous Love*, *Shouting Song*, and many others). Modulations are extremely rare, and the third is usually omitted in the final cadence, with a preference for the open fifth. The *Gospel Trumpet* exemplifies the rarely used fuging style. Sharp dissonances sometimes result from independent melodic lines as in the music of the earlier New England school of composers.

A number of the folk hymns in the *Anthology* have tunes of special interest. Among these are *Fairton*, with its extraordinary use of open fourths and second-inversion chords, irregular phrase-lengths, and unusually attractive melody; *Primrose*, in which the first, second, and fourth phrases begin with the same notes; *Morality*, which is based on the tune known as *Alknomook* (No. 77); *The Hebrew Children*, which was one of the many tunes taken over by the Negroes that became "spirituals" (No. 97a); the tune of *Kedron* (No. 95), which is found in modern church hymnals; *Plenary*, a setting of *Auld Lang Syne;* and *Wondrous Love*, one of the finest examples of a folk-hymn melody.

The *Shouting Song* and *Good Old Way* are typical examples of revival spirituals with a short, simple tune for the leader followed by a camp-meeting chorus for the entire group. *The Converted Thief* is a religious folk ballad in which the story was originally sung by one voice.

The Southern folk hymn gradually gave way to the commercialized "gospel song" with its sentimental text and stereotyped music with a catchy rhythm. Camp-meeting singing of folk hymns, however, has been preserved in many rural communities in the South, and in recent years there has been a renewed interest in this music as there has been in other indigenous music of America.

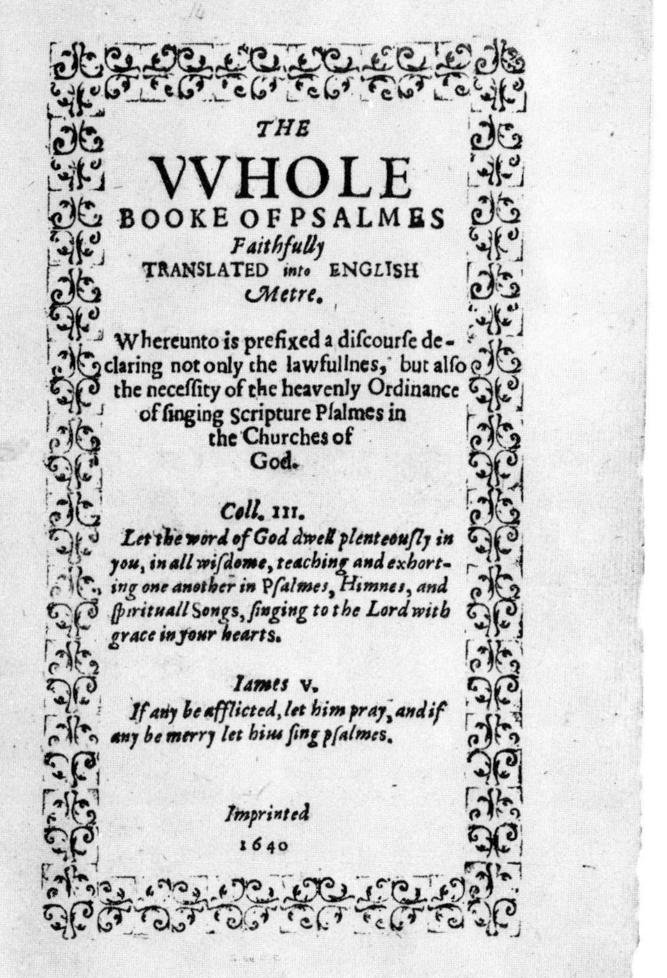

THE

VVHOLE

BOOKE OF PSALMES

Faithfully

TRANSLATED *into* ENGLISH

Metre.

Whereunto is prefixed a discourse declaring not only the lawfullnes, but also the necessity of the heavenly Ordinance of singing Scripture Psalmes in the Churches of God.

Coll. III.

Let the word of God dwell plenteously in you, in all wisdome, teaching and exhorting one another in Psalmes, Himnes, and spirituall Songs, singing to the Lord with grace in your hearts.

Iames v.

If any be afflicted, let him pray, and if any be merry let him sing psalmes.

Imprinted

1640

Title page from the first edition of the *Bay Psalm Book* (Cambridge, 1640).

Low Dutch Tune from the *Bay Psalm Book* (Boston, 1698).
See No. 13, p. 34.

And so he died in the flesh,
But quickned in the spirit:
His body then was buried,
As is our vse and right.
His spirit after this descend
Into the lower parts:
To them that long in darknesse were,
The true light of their hearts.

And in the third day of his death,
He rose to life againe:
To the'nd he might be glorified,
Out of all griefe and paine:
Ascending to the heauens hie,
To sit in glory still.

On Gods right hand his father deere,
According to his will.

Vntill the day of iudgement come,
When he shall come againe:
with Angels, power, yet of that day
We all be vncertaine.
To iudge all people righteously,
Whom he hath dearely bought:
The liuing and the dead also,
Which he hath made of nought.

And in the holy spirit of God,
My faith to satisfie:
The third person in Trinitie

A Prayer to the holy Ghost. CANTVS. John Milton.

Come holy spirit the God of might, comforter of vs all: Teach vs to know thy word aright, that we doe neuer fall.

Yorke Tune. TENOR, or Playnsong.

Come holy spirit the God of might, comforter of vs all: Teach vs to know thy word aright, that we doe neuer fall.

O holy Ghost visit our coast,
defend vs with thy shield:
Against all sinne and wickednesse,
Lord help vs winne the field.

Lord keepe our King and his Counsell,
and giue them will and might
To perseuere in thy Gospell,
which can put sinne to flight:
O Lord which giuest thy holy word,
send preachers plenteously:
That in the same we may accord,
and therein liue and die.

O holy Spirit direct aright,
the preachers of thy word:
That thou by them maist cut downe sinne
as it were with a sword.
Depart not from those pastors pure,
but aide them at all neede:
Which breake to vs the bread of life,
whereon our soules doe feede.

O Blessed Spirit of truth keepe vs

Da pacem. CANTVS. Tho. Rauens. B. of M.

Giue peace in these our dayes O Lord, great dangers are now at hand:

2. High Dutch Tune. TENOR, or Faburden.

Giue peace in these our dayes O Lord, great dangers are now at hand:

Beleeue I stedfastly.
The holy and Catholike Church,
That Gods word doth maintaine?
And holy Scripture doth allow,
Which Satan doth disdaine.

And also I doe trust to haue,
By Iesus Christ his death:
Release and pardon for my sins,
And that onely by faith.
What time all flesh shall rise againe
Before the God of might:
And see him with their bodily eyes,
Which now doth giue them light.

And then shall Christ our Sauiour,
The Sheepe and Goats diuide:
And giue life euerlastingly
To those whom he hath tride.
Within his realme celestiall,
In glory for to rest:
With all the holy company,
Of Saints and Angels blest.

Which serue the Lord omnipotent,
Obediently each houre:
To whom be all dominion,
And prayse for euermore.

A Prayer to the holy Ghost. MEDIVS. John Milton.

Come holy Spirit the God of might comforter of vs all. Teach vs to know thy word aright, that we doe ne- uer fall.

BASSVS.

Come holy spirit the God of might, comforter of vs all: Teach vs to know thy word aright, that we doe neuer fall.

in peace and vnitie:
Keepe vs from sects and errours all,
and from all Papistry.

In our time giue thy peace (O Lord)
to nations farre and ne:
And teach them all thy holy word,
that we may sing to thee.

Conuert all those that are our foes,
and bring them to thy light:
That they and we may well agree,
and prayse thee day and night.
O Lord increase our faith in vs,
and loue so to abound:
That man and wife be void of strife,
and neighbours about vs round.

All glory to the Trinitie,
that is of mighties most:
The liuing Father and the Sonne,
and eke the holy Ghost.
As it hath beene in all the time,
that hath beene heretofore:
As it is now, and so shall be,
henceforth for euermore.

Da pacem. MEDIVS. Tho. Rauens. B. of M.

Giue peace in these our daies O Lord, great dangers are now at hand:

BASSVS.

Giue peace in these our dayes O Lord, great dangers are now at hand:

S 2

A Prayer to the Holy Ghost (*Yorke Tune*) by John Milton, Sr.
From *The Whole Booke of Psalmes* by Thomas Ravenscroft (London, 1621).
See No. 6, p. 29.

A page from *The Grounds and Rules of Musick Explained*
by Thomas Walter (Boston, 1721).
See No. 25, p. 52.

10

Cant. 85 Psalm *Tune.*

Med.

Bass.

Cant. 100 Psalm *Tune.*

Med.

Bass.

Cant. 100 Psalm *Tune New*

Med.

Bass.

C 2.

A page from *An Introduction to the Singing of Psalm-Tunes*
by John Tufts (Boston, 1726).
See No. 23, p. 50.

GOTT ein Herrscher aller Heyden, der sein Volck bald wird herrlich leiten, und ihr Recht lassen hoch hergehn: wenn ER Zion schön wird schmücken, ihr Heil wird lassen naher rücken, so wird man Freud und Wonne sehn

an Seinem Eigenthum, das nun giebt Preiß und Ruhm GOTT dein König, der sie erhöht, ihr Völcker seht! wie GOttes Braut nun einhergeht. 196.

Gott ein Herrscher aller Heyden by Johann Conrad Beissel (Ephrata, 1747).
See No. 31, p. 64.

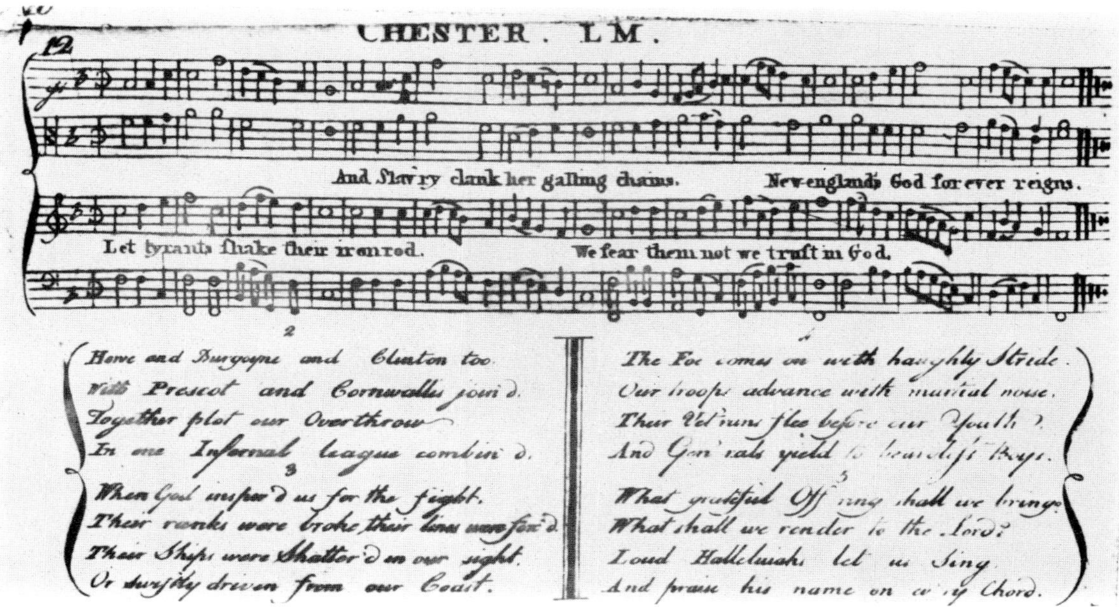

Chester by William Billings. From *The Singing Master's Assistant* (Boston, 1778).
See No. 43, p. 112.

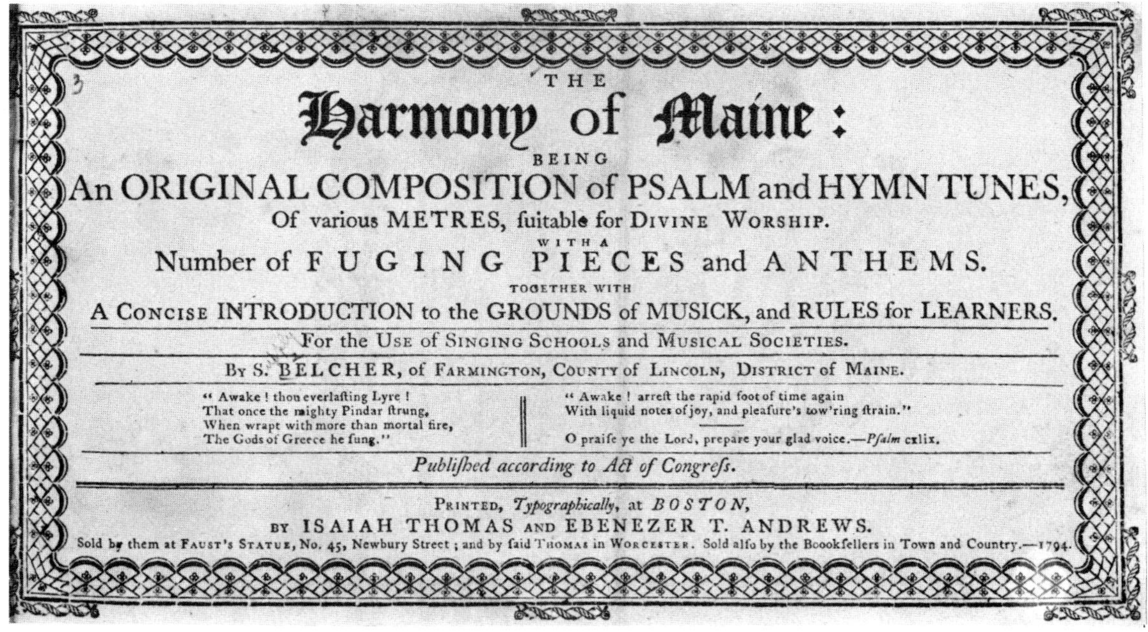

THE
Harmony of Maine:
BEING
An ORIGINAL COMPOSITION of PSALM and HYMN TUNES,
Of various METRES, ſuitable for DIVINE WORSHIP.
WITH A
Number of FUGING PIECES and ANTHEMS.
TOGETHER WITH
A CONCISE INTRODUCTION to the GROUNDS of MUSICK, and RULES for LEARNERS.
For the USE of SINGING SCHOOLS and MUSICAL SOCIETIES.
BY S. BELCHER, of FARMINGTON, COUNTY of LINCOLN, DISTRICT of MAINE.

"Awake! thou everlaſting Lyre!
That once the mighty Pindar ſtrung,
When wrapt with more than mortal fire,
The Gods of Greece he ſung."

"Awake! arreſt the rapid foot of time again
With liquid notes of joy, and pleaſure's tow'ring ſtrain."
O praiſe ye the Lord, prepare your glad voice.—*Pſalm* cxlix.

Publiſhed according to Act of Congreſs.

PRINTED, *Typographically*, at *BOSTON*,
BY ISAIAH THOMAS AND EBENEZER T. ANDREWS.
Sold by them at FAUST'S STATUE, No. 45, Newbury Street; and by ſaid THOMAS in WORCESTER. Sold alſo by the Bookſellers in Town and Country.—1794.

Title page of Supply Belcher's *The Harmony of Maine* (Boston, 1794).
See No. 59, p. 154.

The first page of the Adagio from the original manuscript of the *Sonata in E for the Piano Forte* by Alexander Reinagle.
See No. 74, p. 191.

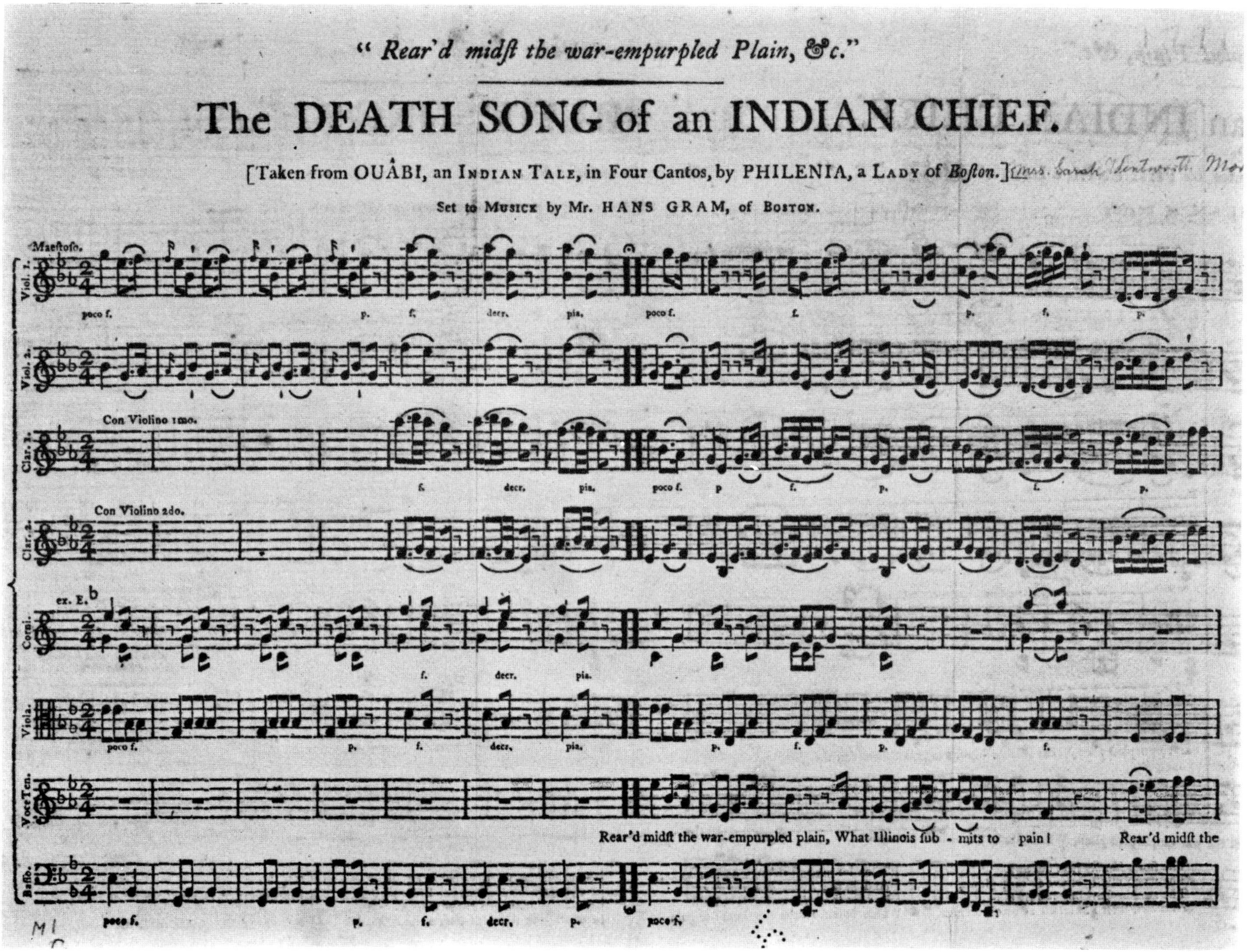

"*Rear'd midst the war-empurpled Plain, &c.*"

The DEATH SONG of an INDIAN CHIEF.

[Taken from OUÂBI, an INDIAN TALE, in Four Cantos, by PHILENIA, a LADY of *Boston*.]

Set to MUSICK by Mr. HANS GRAM, of BOSTON.

Maestoso.

Viol. 1. · Viol. 2. · Clar. 1. (Con Violino 1mo.) · Clar. 2. (Con Violino 2do.) · Corni. (ex. E. b) · Viola. · Voce Ten. · Basso.

Rear'd midst the war-empurpled plain, What Illinois sub - mits to pain! Rear'd midst the

The original score of *The Death Song of an Indian Chief* by Hans Gram.

See No. 80, p. 222.

The original edition of *The Star Spangled Banner*, adapted an

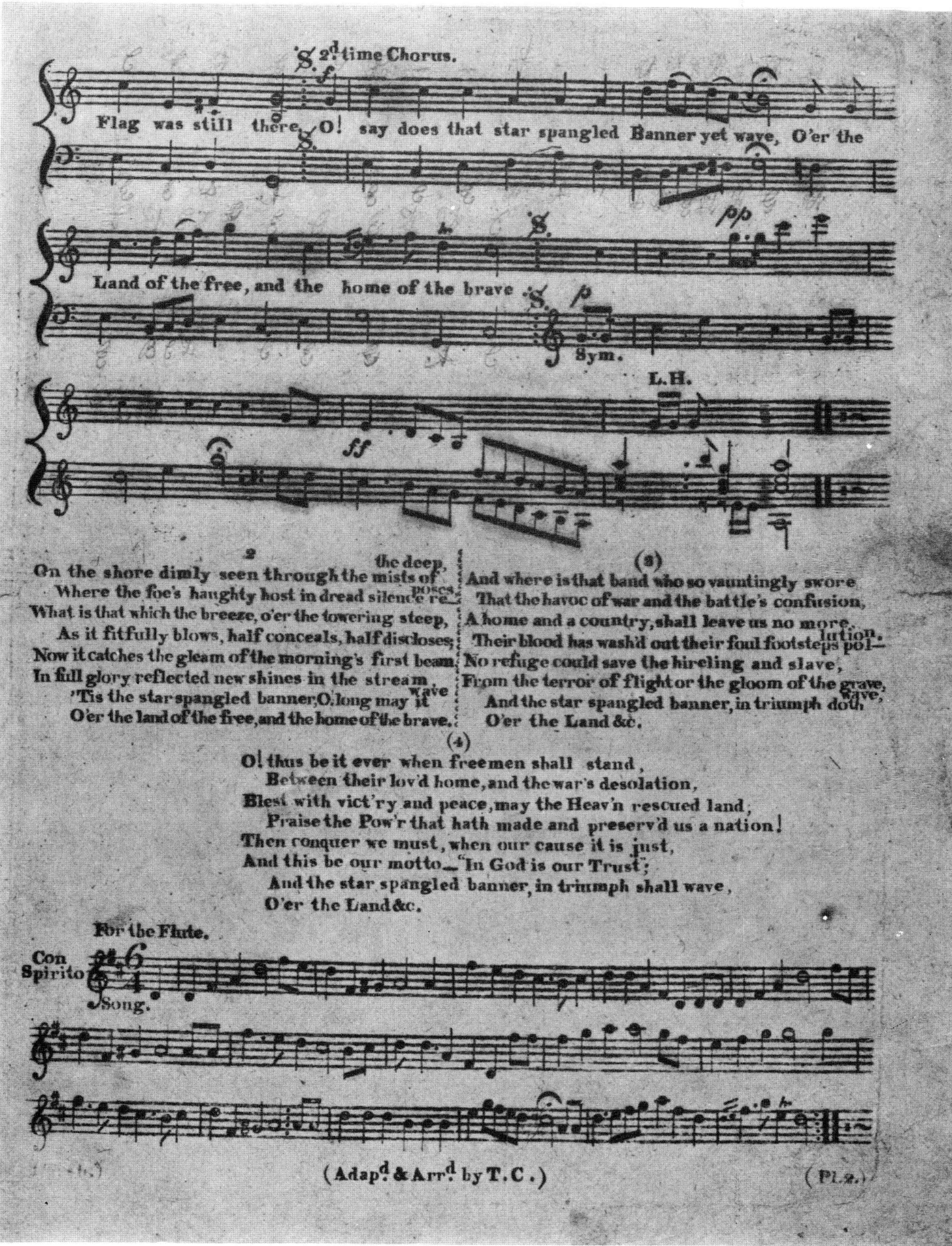

ranged by Thomas Carr (Baltimore, 1814). *See No. 115, p. 291.*

Cover page showing "Mr. T. Rice As the Original Jim Crow" (c. 1830).
See No. 104, p. 262.

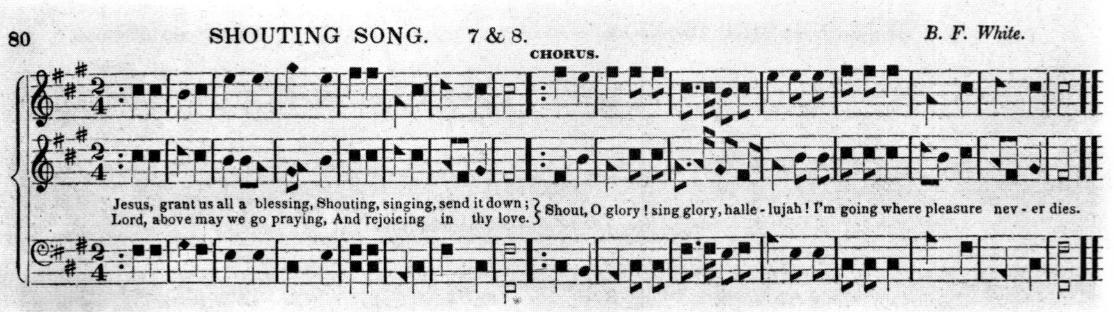

Shouting Song by Benjamin Franklin White.
From *The Sacred Harp* by B. F. White and E. J. King (Philadelphia, 1844).
See No. 102, p. 258.

Cover page of *The Old Arm Chair* by Henry Russell (Boston, 1840).
See No. 123, p. 313.

Cover page of *The Banjo* by Louis Moreau Gottschalk (New York, 1855).
See No. 125, p. 323.

91. FAIRTON

1813

Repository of Sacred Music, Part Second
John Wyeth
(*Harrisburg, Pa., 1820*)

Elkanah K. Dare
(1782–1826)

[1] This note is F-sharp in the original.

2

Give me the presence of thy grace,
  Then my rejoice tongue
Shall speak aloud thy righteousness,
  And make thy praise my song.

4

A soul oppres'd with sin's desert,
  My God will ne'er despise;
A humble groan, a broken heart,
  Is our best sacrifice.
Ps. 51: Isaac Watts (1719)
(1674–1748)

92. MORALITY

1789

The Missouri Harmony
Allen D. Carden
(*Cincinnati, 1820*)

4

For when age steals on me, and youth is no more,
And the moralist time shakes his glass at my door,
What pleasure in beauty or wealth can I find?
My beauty, my wealth, is a sweet peace of mind.

6

And when I the burden of life shall have borne,
And death with his sickle shall cut the ripe corn,
Reascend to my God without murmur or sigh,
I'll bless the kind summons, and lie down and die.

93. CONSOLATION

1813

The Missouri Harmony
Allen D. Carden
(*Cincinnati, 1820*)

Dean?

[1] G in the Bass in the original.
[2] Thus in the original.

2

Night unto night his name repeats,
The day renews the sound,
Wide as the heav'n on which he sits,
To turn the seasons round.

6

Dear God, let all my hours be thine,
Whilst I enjoy the light;
Then shalt my sun in smiles decline,
And bring a pleasant night.

Hymn: Isaac Watts (1707)
(1674–1748)

94. PRIMROSE

Twenty-fourth

1813

Kentucky Harmony
Ananias Davisson
(*Harrisonburg, Va., 1821*)

[Amzi] Chapin

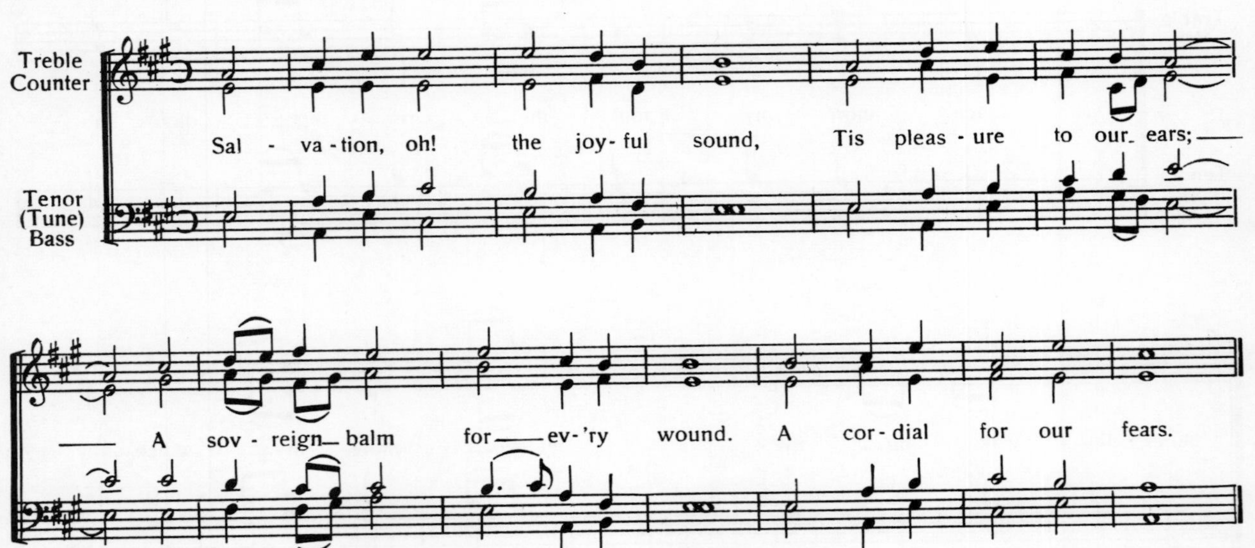

2

Buried in sorrow and in sin
At hell's dark door we lay,
But we arise by grace divine,
To see a heav'nly day.

3

Salvation! let the echo fly
The spacious world around,
While all the armies of the sky
Conspire to raise the sound.

Hymn: Isaac Watts (1707)
(1674–1748)

95. KEDRON

1799

The United States Harmony
Amos Pilsbury
(*Boston, 1799*)

Anonymous

95a. KEDRON

1835

The Southern Harmony
William Walker
(*New Haven, 1835*)

[Elkanah K.] Dare
(1782–1826)

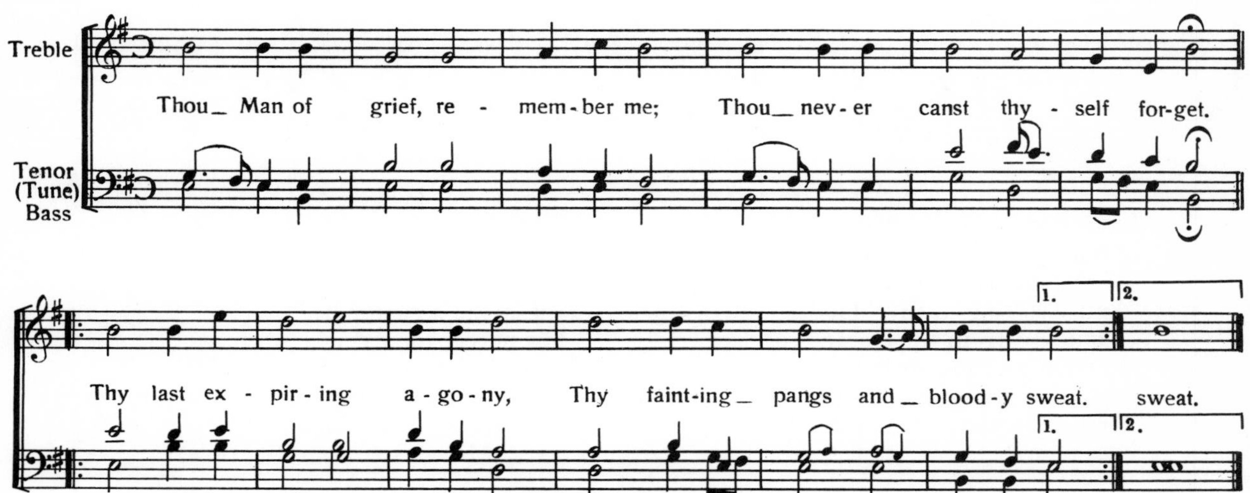

96. THE CONVERTED THIEF

1835

The Southern Harmony [William] More
William Walker
(*New Haven, 1835*)

2

"Jesus, thou Son and heir of Heav'n!
  Thou spotless Lamb of God!
I see thee bathed in sweat and tears,
  And welt'ring in thy blood.
Yet quickly from these scenes of woe
  In triumph thou shalt rise;
Burst thro' the gloomy shades of death,
  And shine above the skies."

3

"Amid the glories of that world,
  Dear Saviour, think on me,
And in the victories of thy death,
  Let me a sharer be."
His prayer the dying Jesus hears,
  And instantly replies,
"Today thy parting soul shall be
  With me in Paradise."

Mercer's *Cluster* (c. 1815)

97. THE HEBREW CHILDREN

1841

The Southern Harmony
William Walker
(*Philadelphia, 1847*)

David Walker

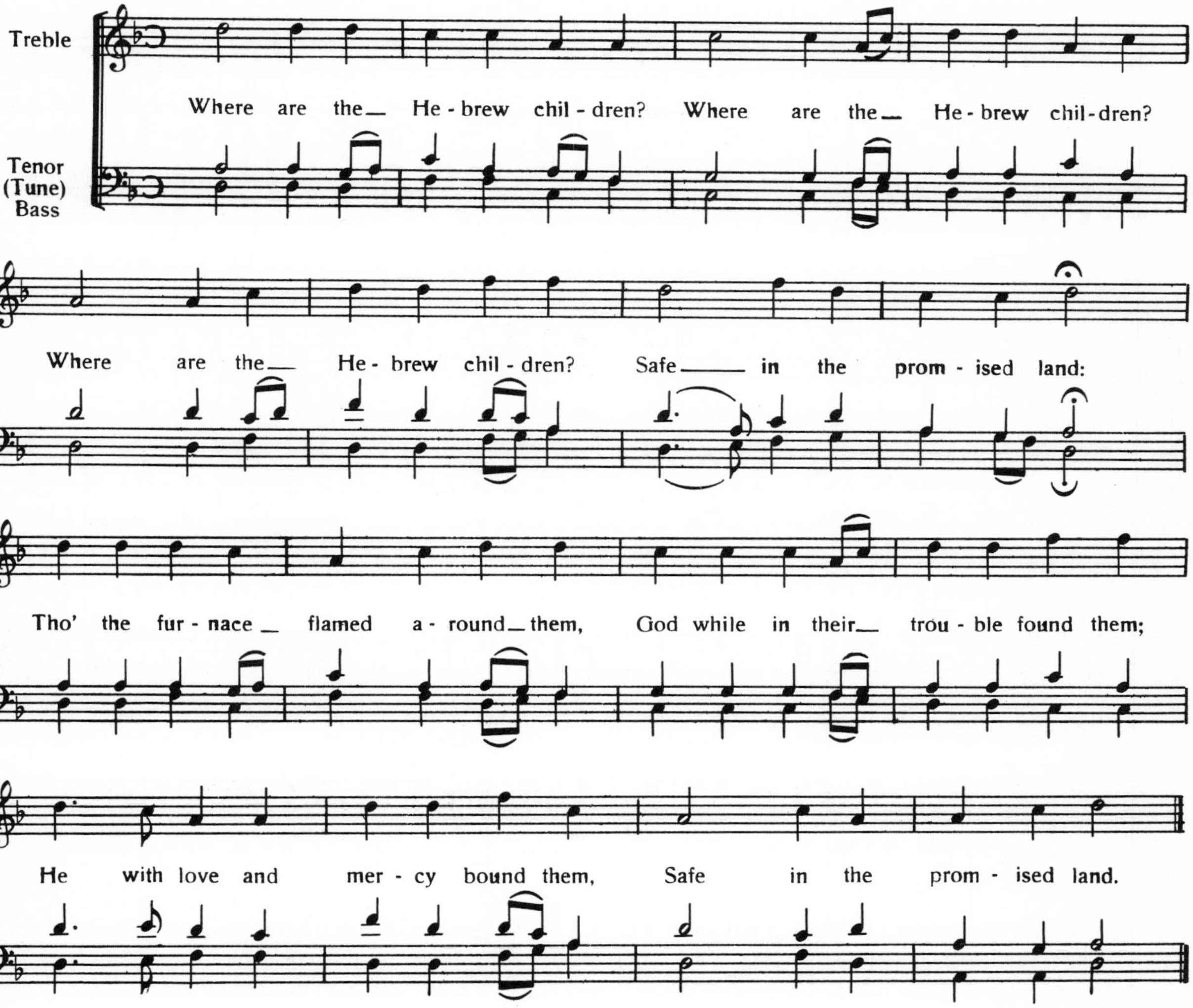
Treble
Tenor (Tune) Bass
Where are the — He - brew chil - dren? Where are the — He - brew chil - dren?
Where are the — He - brew chil - dren? Safe — in the prom - ised land:
Tho' the fur - nace — flamed a - round — them, God while in their — trou - ble found them;
He with love and mer - cy bound them, Safe in the prom - ised land.

97a. NEGRO SPIRITUAL

based on
The Hebrew Children

Won - der where is good ole Dan - iel, Won - der where is good ole Dan - iel, —
Won - der where is good ole Dan - iel, Way o - ver in de prom - ise lan'.

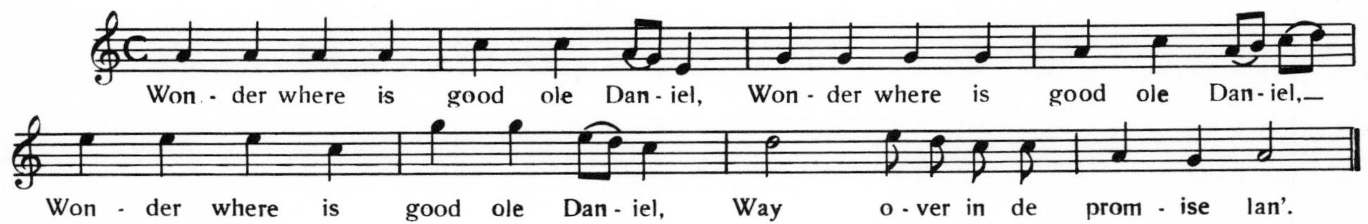

98. THE GOOD OLD WAY

1835

The Southern Harmony
William Walker
(*New Haven, 1835*)

William Walker
(1809–1875)

2

Our conflicts here, though great they be,
Shall not prevent our victory,
If we but watch, and strive, and pray,
Like soldiers in the good old way.

Chorus

And I'll sing hallelujah,
  And glory be to God on high;
And I'll sing hallelujah,
  There's glory beaming from the sky.

3

O good old way, how sweet thou art!
May none of us from thee depart,
But may our actions always say,
We're marching on the good old way.
  And I'll sing, etc.

6

Ye valiant souls, for heaven contend;
Remember glory's at the end;
Our God will wipe all tears away,
When we have run the good old way.
  And I'll sing, etc.

99. PLENARY

1835

The Southern Harmony — A. Clark

William Walker

(*New Haven, 1835*)

2

"Princes, this clay must be your bed,
In spite of all your towers;
The tall, the wise, the reverend head
Must lie as low as ours"!

3

Great God! is this our certain doom?
And are we still secure?
Still walking downward to the tomb,
And yet prepare no more!

4

Grant us the power of quickening grace,
To fit our souls to fly;
Then, when we drop this dying flesh,
We'll rise above the sky.

Hymn: Isaac Watts (1707)
(1674–1748)

100. NEW BRITAIN

Amazing Grace

1835

The Southern Harmony
William Walker
(*New Haven, 1835*)

2

'Twas grace that taught my heart to fear,
And grace my fears relieved:
How precious did that grace appear,
The hour I first believed!

3

Thro' many dangers, toils, and snares,
I have already come;
'Tis grace has brought me safe thus far,
And grace will lead me home.

John Newton (1789)
(1725–1807)

101. WONDROUS LOVE

1835

The Southern Harmony
William Walker
(*New Haven, 1835*)

Christopher

[1] This note is F in the original.
[2] This note is F in the original.

2

When I was sinking down, sinking down, sinking down,
When I was sinking down, sinking down,
When I was sinking down
Beneath God's righteous frown
Christ laid aside His crown for my soul, for my soul,
Christ laid aside His crown for my soul.

4

And when from death I'm free I'll sing on, I'll sing on,
And when from death I'm free I'll sing on,
And when from death I'm free
I'll sing and joyful be,
And thro' eternity I'll sing on, I'll sing on,
And thro' eternity I'll sing on.

102. SHOUTING SONG

1844

The Sacred Harp
B. F. White and E. J. King
(*Philadelphia, 1844*)

Benjamin Franklin White
(1800–1879)

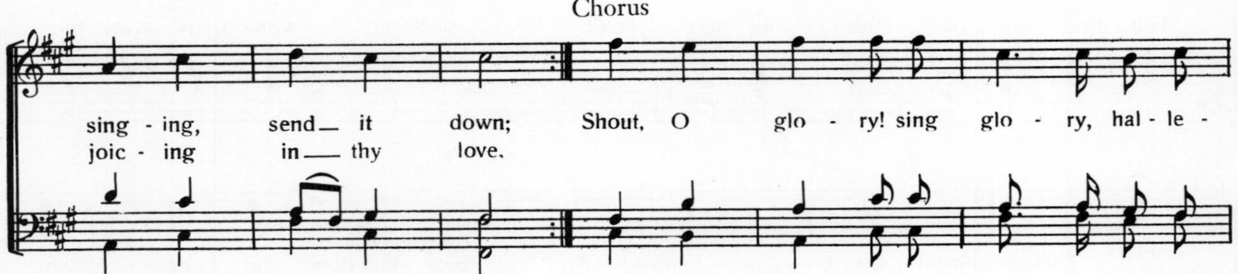

103. GOSPEL TRUMPET

1844

The Sacred Harp
B. F. White and E. J. King
(*Philadelphia, 1844*)

E. J. King
(c. 1800–c. 1850)

Chapter Eight

MUSIC OF THE MINSTREL SHOWS

De Scriber am pressed wid de vast 'sponsibility ob pesentin' to de whole Popalashun ob dis world de genus ob de colored pofessors ob de' vine art; and did he tink dat de world would be safe widout em, an' dat posterity would not sink down into oblivion, he would most 'spectfully hab declined de honor to be fus' skientific orther ob an Ethiopian Glee Book.

Preface, *The Ethiopian Glee Book* (Boston, 1848)

MINSTREL shows (often called Ethiopian operas) and ballad operas have much in common. Perhaps the most binding feature is their use of borrowed music, which, interspersed as needed, shared the proceedings on the stage with dances, comic repartees, stump speeches, and jokes. The performers with blackened faces, dressed in striped trousers, swallow-tail coats, oversized collars, and wearing white gloves, are often pictured seated in a semicircle singing to the accompaniment of a banjo, violin, tambourine, and bones (castanets). The beginning of the minstrel show can be traced back to about 1820, when white performers impersonated the southern Negro plantation workers and the northern Negroes who tried to imitate the white man.

The songs included in the *Anthology* are among the most popular and were performed by such bands as Bryant's Minstrels, Virginia Serenaders, Sable Harmonists, Christy's Minstrels, and Ethiopian Serenaders, to name but a few. Thomas ("Daddy") Rice, A. F. Winnemore, Stephen Foster, and Dan Emmett were fully aware of the publicity and sales opened to their music by the minstrels—the precursors of our contemporary disc-jockeys. Appropriated by these, the songs were catapulted into the realm of immortality. Typical of the minstrel song is the solo-chorus formula with repeated refrains sung in unison or in three or four parts over a simple accompaniment. The song, in a major key, is preceded by an introduction or "vamp" and ends with a "tag," the melody of which may or may not have been drawn from the song.

The "walk-around" was the finale of the minstrel show. The entire troupe assembled on the stage in a semicircle; a few members stepped forward and sang a stanza, during which they were interrupted by "end-men." Then the whole company joined in the final chorus as some danced, some sang, and others clapped or stamped in time with the music. Originally the walk-around was only a dance; later (about 1858) it was danced and sung, and with Bryant's Minstrels it achieved its popularity as the grand finale.

Jim Crow (No. 104), also known as *Jump, Jim Crow,* was perhaps the first black-face song with a dance act to become the mainstay of the minstrel show. In his attempt to impersonate an old deformed Negro called Jim Crow, "Daddy" Rice wrote this short, simple piece which became an overnight sensation.

The tune *Zip Coon* (No. 105), better known as *Turkey in the Straw,* may be of Irish origin, but certainly there is no doubt that in its one hundred and thirty years of existence in the United States it has become a strictly American tune, ideal for square dances. The song was published in Baltimore in 1834 and introduced at the Bowery Theatre in New York by Bob Farrell. Another black-face entertainer, George Washington Dixon, also helped to popularize the tune, and both he and Farrell claimed authorship of the song.

Stop That Knocking at My Door (No. 106) by A. F. Winnemore is a minstrel song for solo voice, with a few spoken words, a duet, and a chorus. The title page bears the information that the song was "sung and arranged by the Christy Minstrels."

Stephen Foster was only twenty-one when he composed one of his first successes, the "non-sense" song, *Oh! Susanna* (No. 107). It was first performed at Andrew's "Eagle Ice Cream Saloon" in Pittsburgh in 1848, and a year later it was taken over by Christy's Minstrels. The tune became one of the most popular of its day, and it was even carried to California by the forty-niners, who adopted it as their theme song.

Old Folks at Home (No. 108) is without doubt Stephen Foster's most famous song. It first appeared in 1852 as an "Ethiopian Melody as sung by Christy's Minstrels. Written and Composed by E. P. Christy." Not until the song won an incredible popularity both in England and in America did Foster acknowledge himself as the composer. This nostalgic song, written about a plantation on the Suwannee river [1] (Foster spelled it "Swanee"), which he had never seen, offers a sharp contrast to the gay and lively tunes usually associated with the minstrels. It does, however, retain the form of the typical Ethiopian song —namely, three or four stanzas for a solo voice, each followed by a refrain for the chorus.

Dixie's Land (No. 109) was composed by Dan Emmett in 1859 when he was a member of Bryant's Minstrels, and it became a favorite walk-around. The tune achieved such great popularity that it was adopted by the Confederate Army as a battle-song along with *The Bonnie Blue Flag.*

[1] The Suwannee river rises in Georgia and flows through Northern Florida into the Gulf of Mexico.

104. JIM CROW

c. 1830

Thomas Dartmouth Rice
(1808–1860)

[1] D in the original.
[2] E in the original.
[3] E in the original.

2

I'm a rorer on de fiddle,
  And down in ole Virginny;
Dey say I play de skientific.
  Like massa Pagganninny.

12

O den I go to Washinton,
  Wid bank memorial;
But find dey tork sich nonsense,
  I spen my time wid Sal.

15

I den go to de Presiden,
  He ax me wat I do;
I put de veto on de boot,
  An nullefy de shoe.

17

O den I goes to New York,
  To put dem rite all dare;
But find so many tick heads,
  I gib up in dispair.

19

I take de walk to Niblows,
  Wid Dina by my side;
And dare we see Miss Watson,
  De Paganini bride.

20

She sing so lubly dat my heart,
  Went pit a pat jis so;
I wish she fall in lub wid me,
  I'd let Miss Dina go.

105. ZIP COON

1834

Published by G. Willig, Jr.
(*Baltimore, 1834*)

Anonymous

6

Dat tarnal critter Crocket, he never say his prayers,
He kill all de wild cats de Coons and de Bears,
An den he go to Washington to help to make de laws,
An dere he find de Congress men sucking of deir paws.

9

O glory be to Jackson, for he blow up de Banks,
An glory be to Jackson, for he many funny pranks,
An glory be to Jackson, for de battle of Orleans,
For dere he gib de enemy de hot butter beans.

106. STOP THAT KNOCKING AT MY DOOR

1843

A. F. Winnemore

A. F. Winnemore

town, Her eyes so bright dey_ shine at night when de moon am gone_ a
f
way, She used to_ call his dark-ey up Just a fore de broke of
day: wid a who dar? who dar? who dar? An a who dar a knocking at my
f
SPOKEN. Why Sam.
door? Am dat you Sam? Am_ dat you Sam? No, you bet-ter stop dat knocking at my
f
SPOKEN. Aint you gwan to let me in?
By Bass Voice

[1] B in the original.

CHORUS

1st. VOICE
2nd. VOICE
TENOR
BASS
PIANO
Stop that knock-ing, stop that knock-ing, stop that knocking, stop that knocking, Oh! you
Stop that knock-ing, stop that knock-ing, stop that knocking, stop that knocking, Oh! you
Stop that knock-ing, stop that knock-ing, stop that knock-ing, stop that knocking, Oh! you
Stop that knock-ing, stop that knock-ing, stop that knock-ing, stop that knocking, No! I'll
bett-er stop that knock-ing at my door. Stop that
bett-er stop that knock-ing at my door. Stop that
bett-er stop that knock-ing at my door. Stop that
nev-er stop that knock-ing at your door. Let me in. Stop that

knock-ing, stop that knock-ing, stop that knock - ing, stop that knock - ing, Oh! you
knock-ing, stop that knock-ing, stop that knock - ing, stop that knock - ing, Oh! you
knock-ing, stop that knock - ing, stop that knock - ing, stop that knock - ing, Oh! you
knock-ing, stop that knock-ing, stop that knock - ing, stop that knock - ing, No! I'll
bett - er stop that knock-ing at my door.
bett - er stop that knock-ing at my door.
bett - er stop that knock-ing at my door.
nev - er stop that knock- ing at your door.
8va
3

2

She was the prettiest yaller Gal
That eber I did see,
She never would go walking,
Wid any Colored man but me.
And when I took my Banjo down,
And played three tunes or more,
All at once I heard, three pretty hard raps
Come bang again my door.
Wid who dar? who dar?
Stop that knocking &c.

3

Oh, de first one dat cum in de room
Was a darkey dressed to death,
He looked just like de showman,
What dey used to call Mackbeth.
He said he was a Californi man,
An just arrived on shore,
I ax him whare fore he cum an rap,
So hard against my door.
Wid who dar? who dar?
Stop that knocking &c.

107. OH! SUSANNA

1848

Stephen Collins Foster

Stephen Collins Foster (1826–1864)

weath - er it was dry, The — sun so hot I
frose to death Sus - an - na dont you cry.
Chorus
1st Voice
Oh! Sus an - na Oh! dont you cry for me I've —
2nd Voice
Oh! Sus - an - na Oh! dont you cry for me I've —
Tenor.
Oh! Sus - an - na Oh! dont you cry for me I've —
Bass
Oh! Sus - an - na Oh! dont you cry for me I've
Piano
Forte

2

I jumped aboard de telegrph [*sic*],
And trabbelled down de riber,
De Lectric fluid magnified,
And Killed five Hundred Nigger.
De bull gine buste, de horse run off,
I realy thought I'd die;
I shut my eyes to hold my breath,
Susana [*sic*], dont you cry.
Oh! Susana &c.

3

I had a dream de odder night,
When ebery ting was still;
I thought I saw Susana,
A coming down de hill.
The buckwheat cake war in her mouth,
The tear was in her eye,
Says I, im coming from de South,
Susana, dont you cry.
Oh! Susana &c.

108. OLD FOLKS AT HOME

Ethiopian Melody

1851

Stephen Collins Foster

Stephen Collins Foster
(1826–1864)

Sad - - ly I roam, Still long - ing for de old plan - ta - tion,
And for de old folks at home.
Chorus
All de world am sad and drea-ry, Eb - ry where I
roam, Oh! dar - keys how my heart grows wea-ry, Far from de old folks at home.

2

All round de little farm I wandered
When I was young,
Den many happy days I squandered,
Many de songs I sung.
When I was playing wid my brudder
Happy was I,
Oh! take me to my kind old mudder,
Dere let me live and die.—*Chorus*

3

One little hut among de bushes,
One dat I love,
Still sadly to my mem'ry rushes,
No matter where I rove.
When will I see de bees a humming
All round de comb?
When will I hear de banjo tumming
Down in my good old home?—*Chorus*

109. DIXIE'S LAND

1860

Dan. D. Emmett

Dan. D. Emmett
(1818–1904)
Arranged by
W. L. Hobbs

Land. In Dix - ie Land whar I was born in, Ear - ly on one fros - ty mornin, Look a -
way! Look a - way! Look a - way! Dix - ie Land.
Chorus
Den I wish I was in Dix - ie, Hoo - ray! Hoo - ray! In Dix - ie Land, I'll
took my stand, To lib an die in Dix - ie, A - way, A - way, A -

2

Old Missus marry "Will-de-weaber,"
Willium was a gay deceaber;
Look away! &c—
But when he put his arm around'er,
He smilled as fierce as a forty-pound'er.
Look away! &c—
Chorus—Den I wish I was in Dixie, &c—

3

His face was sharp as a butchers cleaber,
But dat did not seem to greab'er;
Look away! &c—
Old Missus acted de foolish part,
And died for a man dat broke her heart.
Look away! &c—
Chorus—Den I wish I was in Dixie, &c—

4

Now here's a health to the next old Missus,
An all de galls dat want to kiss us;
Look away! &c—
But if you want to drive'way sorrow,
Come an hear dis song to-morrow.
Look away! &c—
Chorus—Den I wish I was in Dixie, &c—

5

Dar's buck-wheat cakes an 'Ingen' batter,
Makes you fat or a little fatter;
Look away! &c—
Den hoe it down an scratch your grabble,
To Dixie land I'm bound to trabble.
Look away! &c—
Chorus—Den I wish I was in Dixie, &c—

Chapter Nine

NATIONAL AND PATRIOTIC SONGS

1794-1865

When our land is illumined with liberty's smile,
  If a foe from within strikes a blow at her glory,
Down, down with the traitor that dares to defile
  The flag of the stars, and the page of her story!
    By the millions unchained
    Who their birth-right have gained,
  We will keep her bright blazon forever unstained;
And the Star-Spangled Banner in triumph shall wave,
While the land of the free is the home of the brave.

Oliver Wendell Holmes, an added stanza to our National Anthem (April 14, 1872)

THE NATIONAL and patriotic songs sung during our wars with England again offer testimony of the indebtedness to the mother country evinced in *Yankee Doodle* and *To Anacreon in Heaven* (*Star Spangled Banner*). The tune of *God Save the King* was also well known in the Colonies but found its way peacefully into the repertory of national airs with the text *My country, 'tis of thee.* A large number of patriotic songs completely American in spirit, such as *When Johnny comes marching home* and *Marching through Georgia*, emerged during the Civil War.

New Yankee Doodle (No. 110) is of English provenance and was known in the Colonies before the Revolution. Sung by the British during the early days of the war, it was appropriated by the "Yankees" when they routed the "Redcoats" at Concord.

Joseph Hopkinson, son of Francis, is the author of the words to the patriotic song *Hail! Columbia* (No. 111), which was set to the *President's March* composed by Philip Phile in 1793. It was first performed in New

York on April 25, 1798, by the actor Gilbert Fox, at whose request the text was written, and published by Benjamin Carr a few days later. The words were inspired by the undeclared war with France, and *Hail! Columbia* quickly became one of our most popular patriotic songs. Both words and music were taken over into Southern hymnody and it is found in *The Missouri Harmony* (1820), *The Southern Harmony* (1835), and other Southern tunebooks.

Washington's March (No. 112) is the first of many marches to be published in honor of George Washington. The march is known to have been played at a public celebration in Philadelphia in 1794, but it may have been composed and performed before that. The composer is unknown, although the music is sometimes attributed to Francis Hopkinson.

The Anacreontic Song, "To Anacreon in Heav'n" (No. 113), was the constitutional song of the Anacreontic Society of London. The poem, written about 1775 by Ralph Tomlinson, was set to music by a musician whose identity has long been disputed. Addressed to the Grecian poet Anacreon (c. 500 B.C.) and celebrating the delights of Bacchus and Amor, it achieved a popularity so widespread that it reached our shores before the turn of the century. The edition used in the *Anthology* is the first, published in London in 1778 or 1779, and it is included here so that it may be compared with later versions of the tune.

In 1798 Thomas Paine (not related to his namesake, the Anglo-American philosopher and writer) adapted new words to the English drinking song *To Anacreon in Heaven* which he titled *Adams and Liberty* (No. 114), and it was performed in June of the same year at the fourth anniversary of the Massachusetts Charitable Fire Society. The late Richard S. Hill compiled a list of 85 American parodies adapted to *To Anacreon in Heaven* between 1790 and 1818.[1]

The Star Spangled Banner (No. 115) was written by Francis Scott Key on September 14, 1814, immediately following the bombardment of Fort McHenry by the British. It first appeared as a broadside on September 15 bearing the title *Defence of Fort McHenry* and an indication that it was to be sung to the tune *To Anacreon in Heaven.* A short time later the first edition, with both words and music and the title *The Star Spangled Banner*, was printed in Baltimore by [Joseph] Carr. It was, however, not officially declared our national anthem until 1931.

The words to *My country, 'tis of thee* (No. 116) were written in 1831 by the Reverend Samuel Francis Smith of Boston. At the instigation of Lowell Mason, Smith examined many German music books for attractive melodies suitable for children. He selected the melody *Heil dir im Siegerkranz* and wrote his famous poem, naïvely unaware that the tune selected was the British national anthem. The tune, first printed in *Harmonia Anglicana* (London, 1744), has been adopted at one time or another by a number of countries as their official national anthem. Lowell Mason had the song, clad in its new text, performed by children in Park Street Church on July 4, 1831. The singable tune is somewhat in the rhythm and style of a galliard, and it will be noticed that since its first appearance in America in Lyon's *Urania*, the music has undergone slight melodic changes (*Anthology*, No. 40).

The tune of *Glory Hallelujah* (No. 117) was composed by William Steffe sometime before 1855, and it became a rousing camp-meeting song with the text, "Say Brothers, will you meet us?" After the raid on Harper's Ferry in 1859, a new text commemorating the martyr John Brown was set to the tune, and it became the marching song of the Massachusetts volunteers on their way to the battlefields of the South.

Late in 1861 Julia Ward Howe wrote a "new and more dignified text" to the famous tune and submitted it to the editor of the *Atlantic Monthly*, who published it in the February 1862 issue under his own title *The Battle Hymn of the Republic*.

[1] Richard S. Hill, "The Melody of 'The Star Spangled Banner' in the United States before 1820." Offprint from *Essays Honoring Lawrence C. Wroth*, 1951. Washington: The Library of Congress, 1951.

All quiet along the Potomac to-night (No. 118) was composed by John Hill Hewitt in 1861 to a text attributed to Lamar Fontaine of Mississippi. With this song, in which the death of a sentry on duty along the Potomac is romantically and pathetically described, Hewitt achieved a success that placed him in the front rank of ballad composers. Although it was written as a Confederate song, it became popular in the North as well.

Another song of the Civil War, *Tenting on the Old Camp Ground* (No. 119), was composed by a Northerner, Walter Kittredge, soon after he was drafted in 1862. This melancholy song was widely sung by the Hutchinson family, who advertised themselves as the "Tribe of Asa," and it became so popular that it was taken up by the Southern Army as well as the Northern.

When Johnny comes marching home (No. 120), adopted by the North during the Civil War, was composed by the famous bandmaster Patrick Gilmore and published under his pseudonym, Louis Lambert. This enormously popular and vital folksong-like piece is only sixteen measures in length. Its four stanzas are separated by an eight-measure chorus reminiscent of an Irish jig, possibly a part of Gilmore's Irish inheritance.

Marching through Georgia (No. 121) refers to the famous march "from Atlanta to the sea," about 300 miles through Georgia. It was less a campaign than a picnic, for the Union Army encountered no opposition. Henry Clay Work's text is fully descriptive of this memorable event. In ABA form, this jaunty song with its spirited choral refrain is one of the most popular songs to have been inspired by the Civil War.

110. NEW YANKEE DOODLE

1798

James Hewitt

Arranged by
J.[ames] Hewitt
(1770–1827)

2

The only way to keep off war,
And gaard 'gainst persecution,
Is always to be well prepar'd,
With hearts of resolution.
Yankee Doodle, let's Unite,
Yankee Doodle Dandy,
As patriots, still maintain our right,
Yankee Doodle Dandy.

3

Great WASHINGTON, who led us on,
And Liberty effected,
Shall see we'll die or else be free—
We will not be subjected.
Yankee Doodle, guard your coast,
Yankee Doodle Dandy—
Fear not then or threat or boast,
Yankee Doodle Dandy.

4

A Band of Brothers let us be,
While ADAMS guides the nation;
And still our dear bought Freedom guard,
In ev'ry situation.
Yankee Doodle, guard your coast,
Yankee Doodle Dandy—
Fear not then or threat or boast,
Yankee Doodle Dandy.

5

May soon the wish'd for hour arrive,
When PEACE shall rule the nations—
And Commerce, free from fetters prove
Mankind are all relations.
Then Yankee Doodle, be divine,
Yankee Doodle Dandy—
Beneath the Fig tree and the Vine,
Sing Yankee Doodle Dandy.

111. THE FAVORITE NEW FEDERAL SONG
HAIL! COLUMBIA

1798

Joseph Hopkinson
(1770–1842)

Philip Phile
(c. 1734–1793)

For the Voice, Piano Forte, Guittar and Clarinett

who fought & bled in free - doms cause, and when the storm of war was gone, en -
joy'd the _ peace your va - lor won; let In - de - pen - dence be _ our _ boast,
ev - er mind - ful what it cost, ev - er grate - ful for _ the _ prize,
2d time Chorus
let its Al - tar reach the Skies. Firm, u - ni - ted, let _ us _ be,
ral - lying round our Li - ber - ty, as a band of _ Bro - thers joind,

2

Immortal Patriots, rise once more!
Defend your rights, defend your shore;
Let no rude foe with impious hand,
Let no rude foe with impious hand,
Invade the shrine where sacred lies,
Of toil and blood, the well earn'd prize;
While offering peace, sincere and just,
In heav'n we place a manly trust,
That truth and justice will prevail,
And every scheme of bondage fail!
Firm, united. &c.

3

Sound, sound the trump of fame!
Let Washington's great name
Ring through the world with loud applause!
Ring through the world with loud applause!
Let every clime to Freedom dear
Listen with a joyful ear;
With equal skill, with godlike pow'r,
He governs in the fearful hour
Of horrid war, or guides with ease
The happier times of honest peace.
Firm, united. &c.

4

Behold the Chief who now commands,
Once more to serve his Country, stands
The rock on which the storm will beat!
The rock on which the storm will beat!
But arm'd in virtue, firm and true,
His hopes are fix'd on heav'n and you;
When hope was sinking in dismay,
When glooms obscur'd Columbia's day,
His steady mind, from changes free,
Resolved on Death or Liberty.
Firm, united. &c.

112. WASHINGTON'S MARCH

1794/95

G[eorge] Willig's *Musical Magazine*
(*Philadelphia, 1794/95*)

[1] The trills (tr) and the sign (∽) may be played  or 
[2] The original has the sign (tr) over the G.

113. THE ANACREONTIC SONG

To Anacreon in Heav'n

1778/79

Ralph Tomlinson

sides, I'll in-struct you like me, to_ in-twine, The Myr-tle of VENUS with BACCHUS'S Vine.
Chorus
And be-sides, I'll in-struct you like me, to en-twine, The
And be-sides, I'll in-struct you like me, to en-twine, The
Myr - tle of— VE - NUS with BAC-CHUS - 'S— Vine."
Myr - tle of VE - NUS with BAC-CHUS - 'S Vine."

114. ADAMS AND LIBERTY

The Boston Patriotic Song

1798

Thomas Paine
(Robert Treat Paine)
(1731–1814)

Air: *Anacreon in Heaven*

[1] The first two bass notes are F in the original.

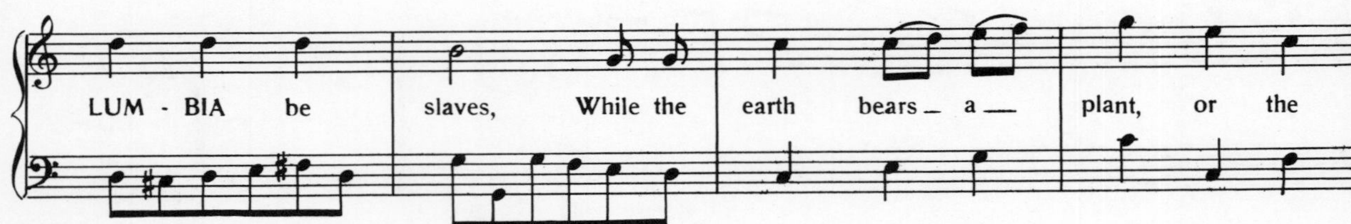

2

In a clime, whose rich vales feed the marts of the world,
Whose shores are unshaken by Europe's commotion,
The Trident of Commerce should never be hurl'd,
To incense the legitimate powers of the ocean.
But should Pirates invade,
Though in thunder array'd,
Let your cannon declare the free charter of TRADE.
For ne'er shall the sons of COLUMBIA be slaves,
While the earth bears a plant, or the sea rolls its waves.

9

Let FAME to the world sound AMERICA's voice;
No intrigue can her sons from their GOVERNMENT sever;
Her Pride is her ADAMS—his LAWS are her CHOICE,
And shall flourish, till LIBERTY slumber forever!
Then unite, heart and hand,
Like Leonidas' band,
And swear to the GOD of the ocean and land,
That ne'er shall the sons of COLUMBIA be slaves,
While the earth bears a plant, or the sea rolls its waves.

115. THE STAR SPANGLED BANNER

A Pa[t]riotic Song

1814

Francis Scott Key
(1779–1843)

Air: *Anacreon in Heaven*
Adapted and arranged by
T.[homas] C[arr]

2

On the shore dimly seen through the mists of the deep,
Where the foe's haughty host in dread silence reposes,
What is that which the breeze, o'er the towering steep,
As it fitfully blows, half conceals, half discloses;
Now it catches the gleam of the morning's first beam,
In full glory reflected now[1] shines in the stream,
'Tis the star spangled banner, O! long may it wave
O'er the Land of the free, and the home of the brave.

3

And where is that band who so vauntingly swore
That the havoc of war and the battle's confusion,
A home and a country, shall leave us no more,
Their blood has wash'd out their foul footsteps pollution.
No refuge could save the hireling and slave,
From the terror of flight or the gloom of the grave,
And the star spangled banner, in triumph doth wave
O'er the Land of the free, and the home of the brave.

4

O! thus be it ever when free men shall stand,
Between their lov'd home, and the war's desolation.
Blest with vict'ry and peace, may the Heav'n rescued land,
Praise the Pow'r that hath made and preserv'd us a nation!
Then conquer we must, when our cause it is just,
And this be our motto—"In God is our Trust";
And the star spangled banner, in triumph shall wave,
O'er the Land of the free, and the home of the brave.

[1] The original text reads "new."

116. MY COUNTRY, 'TIS OF THEE

1831

Samuel Francis Smith (1808–1897)

Tune: *God Save the King* (1744)

[1] The original has F-sharp in the middle voice.

2

My native country! thee,
Land of the noble free,
    Thy name I love;
I love thy rocks and rills,
Thy woods and templed hills;
My heart with rapture thrills,
    Like that above.

3

Let music swell the breeze,
And ring from all the trees
    Sweet freedom's song;
Let mortal tongues awake,
Let all that breathe partake,
Let rocks their silence break,
    The sound prolong.

4

Our father's God! to thee,
Author of liberty!
    To thee we sing;
Long may our land be bright,
With freedom's holy light;
Protect us by thy might,
    Great God, our King!

117. GLORY HALLELUJAH

1861

William Steffe

3

He's gone to be a soldier in the army of the Lord! :||
His soul is marching on.

4

John Brown's knapsack is strapped upon his back, :||
His soul is marching on.

5

His pet lambs will meet him on the way, :||
And they'll go marching on.

6

They will hang Jeff Davis to a tree, :||
As they march along.

Fort Warren, Boston (1859)

THE BATTLE HYMN OF THE REPUBLIC

1862

Julia Ward Howe
(1819–1910)

1

Mine eyes have seen the glory of the coming of the Lord;
He is trampling out the vintage where the grapes of wrath are stored;
He hath loosed the fateful lightning of His terrible swift sword;
His truth is marching on.

2

I have seen Him in the watch-fires of a hundred circling camps,
They have builded Him an altar in the evening dews and damps;
I can read His righteous sentence by the dim and flaring lamps;
His day is marching on.

3

I have read a fiery gospel writ in burnished rows of steel;
"As ye deal with my contemners, so with you my grace shall deal:"
Let the Hero, born of woman crush the serpent with his heel,
Since God is marching on.

4

He has sounded forth the trumpet that shall never call retreat;
He is sifting out the hearts of men before His judgment seat;
Oh, be swift, my soul, to answer Him! be jubilant my feet!
Our God is marching on.

5

In the beauty of the lilies Christ was born across the sea,
With a glory in his bosom that transfigures you and me;
As he died to make men holy, let us die to make men free,
While God is marching on.

118. ALL QUIET ALONG THE POTOMAC TO-NIGHT

1861

Lamar Fontaine

John Hill Hewitt
(1801–1890)

2

"All quiet along the Potomac to-night,"
  Where the soldiers lie peacefully dreaming,
And their tents in the rays of the clear autumn moon,
  And the light of the camp fires are gleaming.
A tremulous sigh, as the gentle night wind
  Thro' the forest leaves slowly is creeping,
While the stars up above, with their glittering eyes,
  Keep guard o'er the army while sleeping.

3

There's only the sound of the lone sentry's tread,
  As he tramps from the rock to the fountain,
And thinks of the two on the low trundle bed,
  Far away in the cot on the mountain.
His musket falls slack—his face, dark and grim,
  Grows gentle with memories tender,
As he mutters a prayer for the children asleep,
  And their mother—"may Heaven defend her."

4

Then drawing his sleeve roughly over his eyes,
He dashes off the tears that are welling;
And gathers his gun close up to his breast,
As if to keep down the heart's swelling.
He passes the fountain, the blasted pine tree,
And his footstep is lagging and weary:
Yet onward he goes, thro' the broad belt of light,
Towards the shades of the forest so dreary.

5

Hark! was it the night wind that rustles the leaves?
Was it the moonlight so wondrously flashing?
It looked like a rifle! "Ha! Mary, good-bye!"
And his life-blood is ebbing and [s]plashing.
"All quiet along the Potomac to-night,"
No sound save the rush of the river;
While soft falls the dew on the face of the dead,
"The Picket's" off duty forever.

119. TENTING ON THE OLD CAMP GROUND

1864

Walter Kittredge — Walter Kittredge

1. We're tent - ing to-night on the old Camp ground, Give us a song to cheer Our
2. We've been tent - ing to-night on the old Camp ground, Thinking of days gone by, Of the
3. We are tired of war on the old Camp ground, Man-y are dead and gone, Of the
4. We've been fight - ing to-day on the old Camp ground, Man-y are ly - ing near;
wear - y hearts, a song of home, And friends we love so dear.
lov'd ones at home that gave us the hand, And the tear that said, "Good bye"!
brave and true who've left their homes, Oth-ers been wound-ed long.
Some are dead and some are dy-ing, Man-y are in tears.
Chorus
Man - y are the hearts that are wear - y to-night, Wish - ing for the war to

cease; Man - y are the hearts look-ing for the right To see the dawn of
peace. Tent-ing to-night, Tent-ing to-night, Tent-ing on the old Camp
Last verse. Dy - ing to-night. Dy - ing to-night, (Omit)
ground.
Last time ppp
Dy - ing on the old Camp ground.
pp
ppp

120. WHEN JOHNNY COMES MARCHING HOME

1863

Louis Lambert
(Patrick S. Gilmore)

Louis Lambert
(Patrick S. Gilmore)
(1829–1892)

Solo
Chorus
Solo
-rah, We'll give him a heart-y wel-come then, Hur-rah, Hur-rah; The
-rah, To wel-come home our dar-ling boy, Hur-rah, Hur-rah; The
-rah, We'll give the he-ro three times three, Hur-rah, Hur-rah; The
rah, Their choic-est treas ures then dis-play, Hur-rah, Hur-rah; And
men will cheer, the boys will shout, The la-dies, they will all turn out,
vil-lage lads and las-sies say, With ro-ses they will strew the way,
lau-rel wreath is rea-dy now, To place up-on his loy-al brow,
let each one per-form some part, To fill with joy the war-riors heart,
Chorus
D.C.
And we'll all feel gay, When John-ny comes march-ing home.
D.C.

121. MARCHING THROUGH GEORGIA

1865

Henry Clay Work

Henry Clay Work (1832–1884)

start the world a - long
com - mis - sa - ry found!
had not seen for years;
'twas a hand - some boast,
hun - dred to the main;
Sing it as we used to sing it,
How the sweet po - ta - toes e - ven
Hard - ly could they be re - strained from
Had they not for - got, a - las! to
Trea - son fled be - fore us, for re -
fif - ty thou - sand strong,
start - ed from the ground,
break - ing forth in cheers,
reck - on with the host,
sis - tance was in vain,
While we were march - ing through Geor - gia.
Chorus
Air.
"Hur - rah! Hur - rah! we bring the Ju - bi - lee! Hur - rah! Hur - rah! the
Alto.
ff
Tenor.
"Hur - rah! Hur - rah! we bring the Ju - bi - lee! Hur - rah! Hur - rah! the
Base.
ff

flag that makes you free!" So we sang the cho - rus from At -
flag that makes you free!" So we sang the cho - rus from At -

lan - ta to the sea, While we were march - ing through Geor - gia.
lan - ta to the sea, While we were march - ing through Geor - gia.

Chapter Ten

ROMANTIC BALLADS AND NATIONALIST COMPOSERS

1821-1857

"I was dreadfully sorry to hear of poor Gottschalk's death. He had a golden touch, and equal to any in the world, I think. But what a romantic way to die!—to fall senseless at his instrument, while he was playing "La Morte." It was very strange. If anything more is in the papers about him you must send it to me, for the infatuation that I and 99,999 other American girls once felt for him, still lingers in my breast."

From the diary of Amy Fay, *Music Study in Germany* (Chicago, 1881).

THE 19TH CENTURY found musicians in the United States actively engaged in various kinds of music-making for large and receptive audiences. Lowell Mason dominated church music, and the English ballad singer Henry Russell, and the American, Septimus Winner, were unbelievably popular. The exotic Louis Moreau Gottschalk, an exponent of the Creole songs of Louisiana and the salon music of Paris, was causing young ladies to swoon with his romantic pianism, and William Mason was introducing sound principles of piano technique, and composing and playing music of popular appeal. Avowed champions of American music arose, among them the Bohemian composer Anton Philip Heinrich and the

American-born William Henry Fry and George F. Bristow.

America could now boast of such organizations as the Handel and Haydn Society of Boston, founded in 1815, the Philharmonic Society of Boston, 1810, the Musical Fund Society of Philadelphia, 1820, and the Philharmonic Society of New York, 1842. The ambitious character of the Handel and Haydn Society is indicated by the fact that in 1823 it commissioned an oratorio from Beethoven, a work that unfortunately failed to materialize. New York City presented operas only two years after they were first performed in Italy and France. Famous European concert artists began to appear in 1848 (some of whom included California on their itinerary), demonstrated their dazzling techniques, and returned to Europe rich. Touring European orchestras presented a repertory of serious and light music, Classic and contemporary, played with impeccable precision and discipline. At the conclusion of their tours, many a group disbanded, its personnel for the greater part remaining in this country, and each member contributing enormously to the musical progress of his community.

One of our most famous songs, *Home! Sweet Home!* (No. 122), was composed by an Englishman, Henry R. Bishop. The words were written by an itinerant American actor, John Howard Payne, during his residence in London. On a commission by the manager of Covent Garden Theatre, Bishop adapted a French play into an opera, *Clari, or, The Maid of Milan*, and it was produced on May 8, 1823, and published in New York in the same year. Although the opera has long since fallen into obscurity, the air *Home! Sweet Home!* has achieved immortality. The melody is presented several times during the opera; it is heard in the overture, it is sung by Clari in the first act, in the third act by the peasants, and lastly by the chorus backstage. The title page of Bishop's score tells us that *Home! Sweet Home!* was "composed and partly founded on a Sicilian Air," and that "the air is from Bishop's collection of *Melodies of various Nations*."

The Old Arm Chair (No. 123), by the Englishman Henry Russell, who came to America in 1833, is typical of the sentimental ballad genre and is one of the earliest examples of a "mother song." Poignant words, a sentimental melody, an overly well-done performance, was Russell's technique to draw torrential applause from his receptive audience. The popularity of the sentimental ballad was enormous, and there were few melodeons and pianos that did not have copies on the music rack. Not everyone, however, was captivated by these drippingly sentimental songs, and Russell and other ballad writers had their critics.

Septimus Winner, a native-born American, credited the tune of his song *Listen to the Mocking Bird* (No. 124) to a colored boy, Richard Milburn, whom he heard whistling it. The song, with its mournful text and cheerful tune, was published under Winner's pen name of Alice Hawthorne and described as "a sentimental Ethiopian ballad." It became popular with both minstrel and ballad singers, and its refrain made it a favorite song for whistlers.

Louis Moreau Gottschalk was America's first internationally known musician and the first American composer to recognize the value of the native music in the United States. When Chopin heard Gottschalk play in Paris in 1845 he predicted that the young boy would become the "king of pianists." This prediction was soon to become a reality, and in Europe, the United States, the Caribbean Islands, and South America Gottschalk met with astounding success as a virtuoso, composer, and matinee idol.

In his compositions Gottschalk used the Creole songs (*Bamboula*) of his native New Orleans, Spanish folk melodies (*Minuit à Seville*), Latin American songs and rhythms (*Souvenir de Porto Rico*), American national airs (*L'Union*), and folk themes (*The Banjo*). Compositions like *The Last Hope* and *The Dying Poet* represent Gottschalk at his worst and were written, as he said, "to please others, even if not myself."

The Banjo (No. 125) was published in 1855,

two years after Gottschalk's return to America from Europe. The introduction and coda bear a strong resemblance to the pentatonic melodies of the Negro Spiritual *Roll, Jordan, Roll* and Stephen Foster's *Camptown Races* (1850); the remainder of *The Banjo* is original. The realistic strumming of the banjo, motoric drive, ostinato figures, and melodic coloration of this brilliant concert piece are skillfully joined to achieve a highly unified and exciting composition.

William Mason's piano pieces were designed for the public taste of his time, in spite of his high ideals as a musician. The Chopinesque *Lullaby*, Opus 10 (No. 126), with its ostinato left-hand figure, is typical of the works that achieved popularity. It is as a piano pedagogue, however, that William Mason will be remembered.

Yankeedoodle [*sic*] is the coda of an extended composition called *The Hickory, or Last Ideas in America* by that eccentric Bohemian champion of American music, Anton Philip Heinrich. The piece (No. 127) is a paraphrase on the famous *Yankee Doodle* tune, which Heinrich first presents in a minor key. However, he fluctuates rapidly from minor to major throughout, introducing some arresting modulations on the 16th-note ostinato beginning in measure 40. Heinrich's penchant for detailed dynamic markings knew no bounds, for almost every note and phrase is minutely explained or modified through the conventional markings.

The libretto used by William Henry Fry for his opera *Leonora* was prepared by his brother, Joseph, who drew his material from Bulwer-Lytton's novel *The Lady of Lyons* (1838). According to the composer, certain changes were made in the scenes and characters for musical reasons. These modifications include the omission of some characters, the increased prominence given to others, and a change of place and time in order to achieve a more romantic setting. The first performance of *Leonora* took place on June 4, 1845, in Philadelphia. The locale of the opera is Spain in 1530. Revengeful Montalvo, a wealthy nobleman spurned by Leonora, persuades Giulio, a poor but handsome peasant, to masquerade as a wealthy prince and to court Leonora. The enterprise leads to marriage. Later, the remorseful Giulio confesses his part in the plot, returns his bride to her father, Valdor, and sails for South America to seek his fortune. Three years elapse and Leonora, believing Giulio will never return, accepts Montalvo's marriage proposal, providing that he save her father from imminent bankruptcy. As the marriage banns are announced, Giulio arrives with the wealth and honors of a successful adventurer. Learning that Leonora still loves him, he makes his presence known and declares himself able to redeem his wife and to save her father from his creditors. The wicked Montalvo sings *My triumph's nigh* (No. 128) as his marriage to Leonora is announced, and the aria, *Every doubt and danger over* (No. 129), sung by Leonora, brings the opera to a joyous conclusion.

Rip Van Winkle is the first opera composed by an American to be based on a libretto of American lore. The librettist, J. W. Shannon, retained the original plot of Washington Irving's legend of Rip Van Winkle, but added a love affair and marriage between Rip's daughter, Alice, and Edward, a British officer. Bristow's opera had its successful première at Niblo's Theatre in New York on September 27, 1855, and ran for four weeks. In spite of its American origin and subject, the music is stylistically Italianate, with an "easy flow of melody, free from effort and spontaneous." The critic in the *Musical World* also wrote that "in none of the arias [or choruses] do we meet with large conception or rich development of ideas; none of them is shaped after a large pattern." The aria, *Alas! they know me not* (No. 130), in ternary form, is sung by Rip in the last act upon his belated return to the village. The opera concludes with an aria, *List! the merry bells are ringing* (No. 131), sung by Alice, followed by a chorus in which the three principals join.

122. HOME! SWEET HOME!

Aria from
Clari, or, The Maid of Milan

1823

John Howard Payne (1791–1852)

Henry R. Bishop (1786–1855)

hal - low us there, Which seek through the world, is ne'er met with else -
where! Home! Home! sweet, sweet, Home! There's
espress.
pp
no place like Home! There's no place like Home!
Largo
tr
Tempo I.
pp
colla voce
ff
più animato
An Ex - ile from Home, Splen-dour daz - zles in
ff
p

espress.
vain! Oh! give me my low - ly thatch'd Cottage a - - gain! The
Birds sing - ing gai - ly that came at my call, Give me them with the
peacè of mind dearer than all. Home! Home! sweet, sweet,
Home! There's no place like Home! There's no place like Home!
Largo
ad libitum
colla voce
pp
ff
ten.

123. THE OLD ARM CHAIR

1840

Eliza Cook
(1818–1889)

Henry Russell
(1812–1900)

dew'd — it with tears, and em - balm'd — it with sighs; 'Tis bound — by a thou - sand
bands — to my heart, Not a tie will break, not a link will start. Would ye
learn the spell, a moth-er sat there, And a sa - cred — thing is that
Old Arm — Chair.
f
p
mf

I sat and watch'd her man - y a day, When her eyes grew dim, and her
locks — were — grey, And I al - most worshipp'd her when she — smil'd And
turn'd from her bi - ble to bless her child. Years — roll'd on but the
last one sped, My i - dol was shatter'd my — earth star fled: I

learnt how much the heart can _ bear, When I saw her _ die in that
f
p
Old Arm _ Chair.
mf
p
'Tis past! 'tis past! but I gaze on it now With quiv-er - ing breath, and
throb - ing _ brow, 'Twas there she nurs'd me, 'twas there she _ died; And

mem - 'ry flows with la - va — tide. Say — it is fol - ly, and
deem me weak, While the scald - ing drops start — down my cheek; But I
love it, I love it, and can not — tear My soul from a moth - er's —
Old Arm — Chair.
f
p
mf

124. LISTEN TO THE MOCKING BIRD

1855

Alice Hawthorne
(Septimus Winner)
(1827–1902)

dream - ing now of — Hal-ly, — For the thought of her is one that nev - er dies: She's
well I yet re - mem-ber, — When we ga-ther'd in the cot-ton side by side; 'Twas
sleep - ing in the — val-ley, — the — val-ley, — the — val-ley; — She's
in the mild Sep - tem-ber, — Sep - tem-ber, — Sep - tem-ber, — 'Twas
sleep - ing in the — val-ley. — And the mock-ing bird is sing-ing where she lies —
in the mild Sep - tem-ber. — And the mock-ing bird was sing-ing far and wide. —
CHORUS
SOLO
Lis-ten to the mock - ing bird, Lis - ten to the mock-ing bird. The
PIANO

mock-ing bird still sing-ing o'er her grave; Lis-ten to the mock-ing bird, Lis-ten to the

mock-ing bird, Still sing-ing where the weep-ing will-ows wave.

QUARTETTE
AIR.
Lis-ten to the mock-ing bird, Lis-ten to the mock-ing bird, The
ALTO.
TENOR.
Lis-ten to the mock-ing bird, Lis-ten to the mock-ing bird, The
BASS.
PIANO.

mock-ing bird still sing-ing o'er her grave: Lis-ten to the mock-ing bird, Lis-ten to the
mock-ing bird still sing-ing o'er her grave; Lis-ten to the mock-ing bird, Lis-ten to the
8va
tr

mock-ing bird, Still sing-ing where the weep-ing will-ows wave.
mock-ing bird, Still sing-ing where the weep-ing will-ows wave.
8va
tr

3

When the charms of spring awaken,
And the mocking bird is singing on the bough,
I feel like one forsaken,
Since my Hally is no longer with me now.

125. THE BANJO

Grotesque Fantasie

1855

Louis Moreau Gottschalk
(1829–1869)

pp
pp
6
6
6
6
cresc.

f
pp
p Très Rythmé
ben misurato
f brillante
8va

[1] The *facilité* (ossia) of 27 measures is omitted here. The cross indicates the thumb, and the other fingers are numbered from 1 to 4.

strepitoso
cresc.
martellato tutta la forza
fff
fff
ff
p subito
p
mf
p
6
6
rfz

rfz
pp
martellato
6
6

[2] The *facilité* (ossia) of 27 measures is omitted here.

ben misurato
cresc.
strepitoso
martellato
tutta la forza
fff
fff
ff
p subito
p
dim.

pp
pp
cres
cen
do
ben misurato e tranquillo
p
dim.

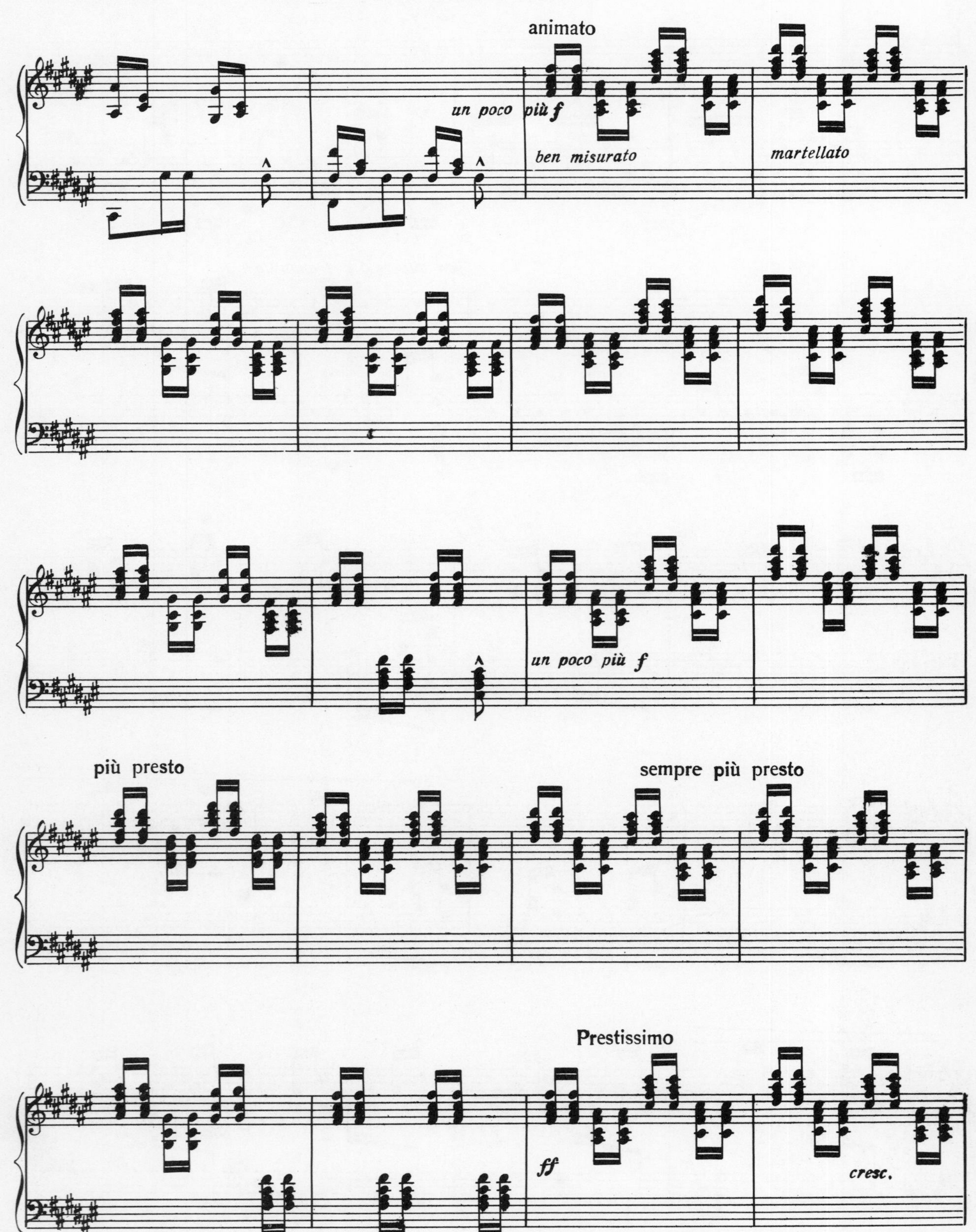

animato
un poco più f
ben misurato
martellato
un poco più f
più presto
sempre più presto
Prestissimo
ff
cresc.

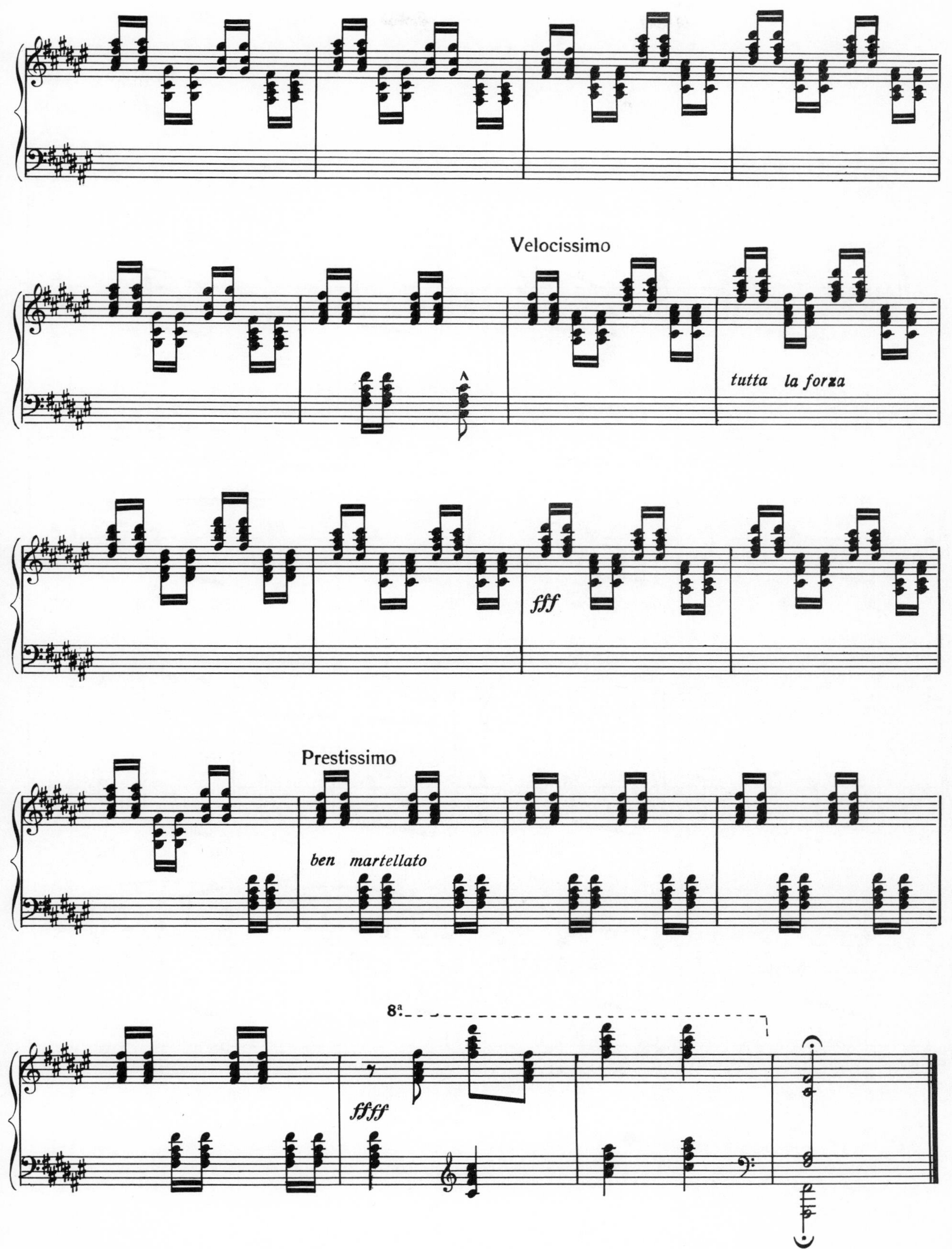
Velocissimo
tutta la forza
fff
Prestissimo
ben martellato
8a
ffff

126. LULLABY

1857

William Mason
(1829–1908)

ten.
poco riten.
a tempo
cresc.
poco riten. e dim.
pp a tempo
poco cresc.
poco cresc.
ten.
sfz
ten.

sfz
pp
poco riten.
a tempo
ten.
sfz
dim:
poco a poco
ritenuto
molto ritard e morendo
pp

127. YANKEEDOODLE

c. 1849

Anthony Philip Heinrich
(1781-1861)

8va
a tempo
mf
p
mf
loco
p
8va
mf
f stringendo

8va
loco
ff
f
mf
tr
p

f
ff
mf
p
mf
f
ff
8va
Adagio
Metronome ♪ = 50
2
p legato
p
pp
tremolante a piacere

128. MY TRIUMPH'S NIGH

Aria from
Leonora

1845

Joseph R. Fry

William Henry Fry
(1815–1864)

con ferocia
con fremito
ni - ted To one whom soon she must ab - hor;
My pride was stung, my pas- sion slight - ed,
voce soffocata
Too deep a wrong to be for - giv - en:
Agitato
Now like my hope shall thine be

blighted, Im - pe - rious, wretch - ed Le - o - nore! Now like my
hope shall thine be blight — ed, Im - pe - rious, wretched Le - o -
- nore! Ah Le - o -
- nore, Im - pe - rious, wretched, wretch - - ed Le - o - nore!
f
p
ff

129. EVERY DOUBT AND DANGER OVER

Aria from
Leonora

1845

Joseph R. Fry

William Henry Fry
(1815–1864)

o - ver, His name — with — glo - - ry light - - ed, Comes my

he - ro and my lov - er ——— To my con - stant ——— arms a -

gain! —— Years of an - guish are all re - qui - - ted In this

mo - ment ——— of ex - ta - tic joy! For by hal - lowed bond u - -

[1] This ornament is written in 16th notes in the original.

130. ALAS! THEY KNOW ME NOT

Aria from
Rip Van Winkle

1855

J. W. Shannon

George Frederick Bristow
(1825–1898)

in the sphere of ma-ny a mile, Full ev-'ry one I know, Not
Clar Oboe
p
con passione
one, not one of these give me a
cresc.
f
dim.
Tutti
poco animato e agitato
smile. Strange fears up-on me grow, Strange
Oboe Fag.
fears up-on me grow, Strange fears up-on me
cresc.
poco cresc.

ff
dim.
grow, Strange fears, strange fears up on — me grow, up -
cresc.
f
ff rit.
tempo
Tutti
dim.
p
mf
- on me grow. — A -
Corno
Clar.
pp
con espress.
- las! a - las they know me not, Stran - gers are they are they — to me, — Am I my -
pp
con anima
self or am I not, — What can the mat-ter, What can the mat - ter be? — Am I my -

cresc.
f
dim.
tempo
mf
-self, or am I not, What can the mat-ter, What can the mat-ter be? Am I my-
Tutti
Corno
cresc.
sf
rit.
tempo
-self, or am I not? Am I my-self, or am I not? What
Tutti
Corno
f
a piacere
dim.
rit.
can the mat - - ter be, What can the mat - - ter
p
pp
a tempo
(Exit Rip.)
pp
be?
tempo
p
legato
dim.
pp

131. LIST! THE MERRY BELLS

Aria and Chorus from
Rip Van Winkle

1855

J. W. Shannon

George Frederick Bristow
(1825–1898)

-round. Gay hearts to the bri - dal
bring - ing, Birds on eve - ry tree are sing - ing, Birds on eve - ry tree are
sing - ing, Glad-ness smiles on all a - round, on all a -
round. All our griefs and woes are end - ing, Peace and hope with joy are
cresc.
ff
mf
pp
p
f
sf

blend - ing, Smiles and bless - ings us at - tend - ing, Love's hap-py heav - en
cresc.
ff

now is found, now is found, is

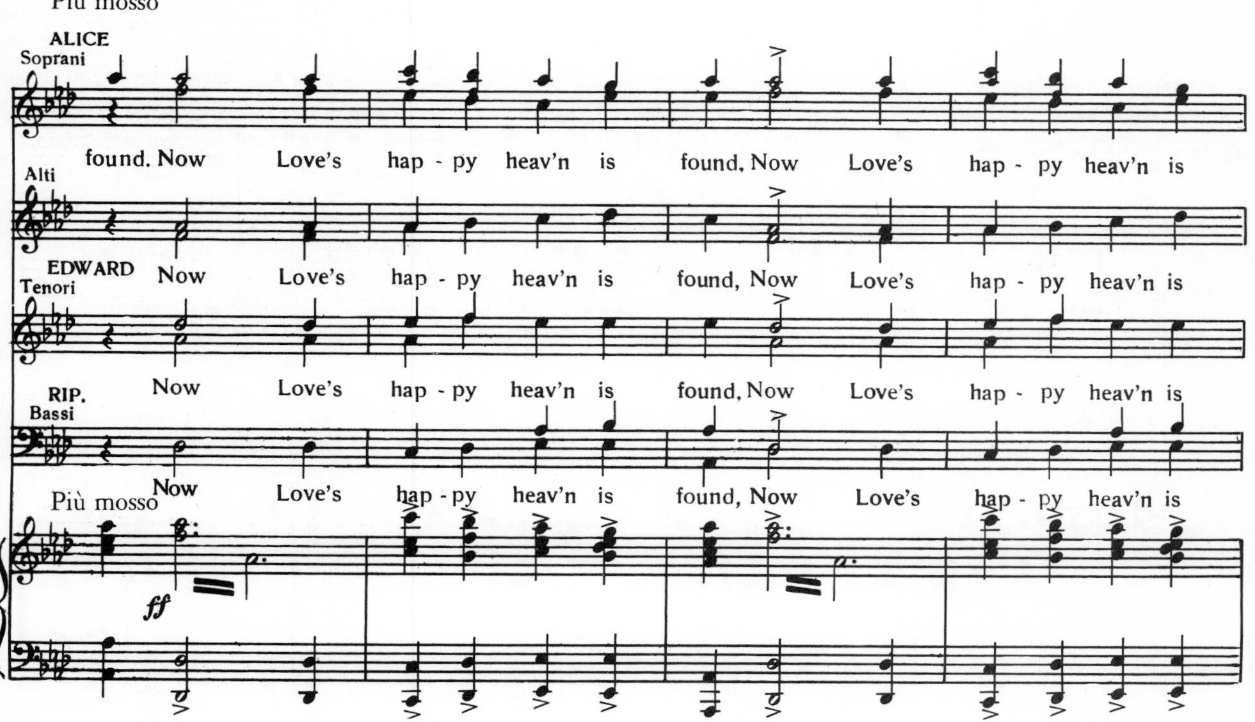
Più mosso
ALICE
Soprani
found. Now Love's hap - py heav'n is found, Now Love's hap - py heav'n is
Alti
Now Love's hap - py heav'n is found, Now Love's hap - py heav'n is
EDWARD
Tenori
Now Love's hap - py heav'n is found, Now Love's hap - py heav'n is
RIP.
Bassi
Now Love's hap - py heav'n is found, Now Love's hap - py heav'n is
Più mosso
ff

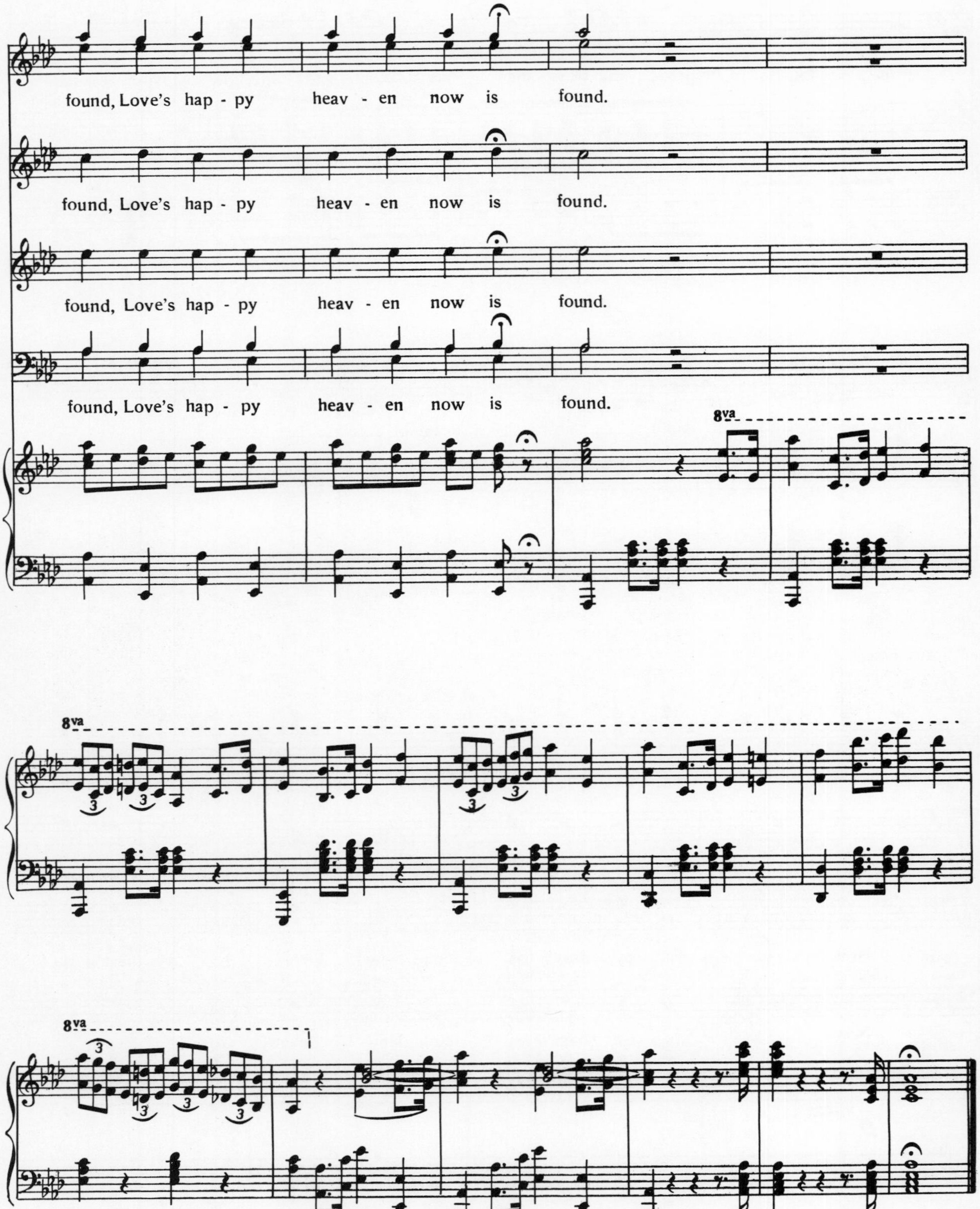

found, Love's hap - py heav - en now is found.

found, Love's hap - py heav - en now is found.

found, Love's hap - py heav - en now is found.

found, Love's hap - py heav - en now is found.

8va

Biographical Notes

John ANTES (b. Frederick, Penn., 1740; d. Bristol, England, 1811) was a Moravian minister, watchmaker, violinmaker, composer, and inventor. In 1752 he was a student in a boys' school in Bethlehem. In 1764 he was called to Herrnhut, Saxony, the international center of the Moravians. He was ordained a Moravian minister in 1769 and spent the years 1770–1781 in Cairo as the first American missionary in Egypt. He returned to Heernhut again and then about 1783 went to Fulneck, England, where he remained for 25 years, moving to Bristol in 1808. Antes is known to have written at least 25 sacred, concerted vocal compositions, thirteen chorales, and three trios for two violins and cello.

Supply BELCHER (b. Stoughton, Mass., 1751; d. Farmington, Maine, 1836), a distinguished man of his time, was a Justice of the Peace, member of the state legislature, school teacher, choir leader, violinist, and composer. He was called by his contemporaries "The Handel of Maine." He fought in the early days of the Revolution, and in 1788 acquired a tavern that became a meeting place for local singers. He attended Billings's singing classes in Stoughton and was strongly influenced by Billings's music. In 1785 Belcher moved to Maine, and in 1794 he published *The Harmony of Maine*. This is his only known publication, and it is devoted entirely to his own compositions.

Daniel BELKNAP (b. Framingham, Mass., 1771; d. Pawtucket, R.I., 1815) began his career as a farmer and mechanic and had little opportunity for instruction in music. He developed his natural voice, however, and soon was teaching singing and the rudiments of music in and near his native town. He published three collections (1797, 1800, 1806), often using his own texts, and a number of his tunes were published by other composer-compilers.

William BILLINGS (b. Boston, 1746; d. there, 1800) was apprenticed to a tanner and, in spite of his love for music, he continued to practice that trade. Ugly in appearance and physically deformed, he was a self-taught, original, and enthusiastic musician, and succeeded in exerting a strong influence on the musical life of New England and beyond. He organized and conducted singing schools and composed and published six collections of music which contained over 250 psalm-tunes and about 50 anthems, almost all sacred music. His popularity, however, did not last; he died in poverty and was buried in an unmarked grave on Boston Common.

Henry Rowley BISHOP (b. London, 1786; d. there, 1855) was a famous opera conductor and composer. He was a professor of music at the Universities of Edinburgh and Oxford and was knighted by Queen Victoria in 1842. Bishop composed about 130 operas (mostly in ballad style), farces, ballets, and various adaptations.

Louis BOURGEOIS (b. Paris, c. 1510; d. there, c. 1561) was a follower of Calvin and lived with him at Geneva from 1545 to 1557, when he returned to Paris. He composed or adapted most of the melodies for Marot's and Bèze's French versifications of the psalms.

William Batchelder BRADBURY (b. York, Maine, 1816; d. Montclair, N.J., 1868) received his first musical instruction from Sumner Hill in Boston. He later became associated with Lowell Mason and George J. Webb of the Boston Academy of Music and after a few years went to Machias, Maine, where he taught singing. He went to New York as an organist and choirmaster, and in 1847 to Leipzig, where he studied for two years with Moscheles and others. In 1854 he joined his brother in the manufacture and selling of pianos. Bradbury edited more than fifty collections of music between 1841 and 1867, and it has been estimated that over 2,000,000 copies of these books were sold.

George Frederick BRISTOW (b. Brooklyn, N.Y., 1825; d. New York, 1898) became a *cause célèbre* when he resigned his position as violinist with the New York Philharmonic Society orchestra in protest over the failure of that Society to perform works by American composers. He was re-engaged a short time later, and in 1856 the Society performed his Second Symphony, in D minor. During the next eighteen years his Third and Fourth Symphonies were programmed. While he was a member of the Philharmonic Society, he conducted the Harmonic Society, and this choral group performed one of his two oratorios, *Praise to God*, among other American works. Bristow also composed two operas, *Rip Van Winkle* and the unfinished *Columbus*, two cantatas, six symphonies, two overtures, two string quartets, anthems, songs, and pieces for organ, piano, and violin.

Benjamin CARR (b. London, 1768; d. Philadelphia, 1831) was the son of Joseph Carr and the brother of Thomas. The three Carrs became successful music publishers and dealers in Philadelphia, where they established a "Musical Repository" in 1793, Baltimore, and New York. Benjamin Carr was editor of the *Musical Journal*, which published his song, *Why, Huntress, why?*, and *The Gentleman's Amusement*, which published *The President's March*, later used for *Hail! Columbia*. He was also active as a composer, singer, organist, and pianist. Carr was associated with Raynor Taylor in the founding of the Musical Fund Society in Philadelphia in 1820, and he was one of the most influential of the European musicians who came to the United States after the Revolution.

A[mzi] CHAPIN may have been an early 19th-century singing master who traveled through Pennsylvania, Virginia, and Kentucky and died in Ohio. His music is found in Wyeth's *Repository, Part Second* and many Southern tunebooks.

William CROFT (b. Warwickshire, England, 1678; d. Bath, 1727) was a chorister in the Chapel Royal and became organist in 1707. He succeeded his master, John Blow, as organist at Westminster Abbey in 1708. Croft was also organist at St. Anne's, Soho, from 1700 to 1712. He composed songs, instrumental music, odes, and music for the services of the church.

Elkanah Kelsay DARE (1782–1826), a Methodist minister and a musician, served for a time as dean of boys at Wilmington College, Delaware.

Eliakim DOOLITTLE (b. Connecticut, 1772; d. Argyle, N.Y., 1850) was active as a composer and singing teacher. His elder brother, Amos, also a musician, was a business partner of Daniel Read.

Jacob ECKHARD (b. Eschwege, Germany, 1757; d. Charleston, S.C., 1833), a church organist and composer, came to America in 1776 and after the Revolution settled in Richmond, where he taught music and was organist at St. John's Episcopal Church. In 1786 he became organist and choir director of the German Lutheran Church in Charleston, and in 1809 he assumed similar duties at St. Michael's Episcopal Church. Here he compiled a manuscript tunebook for the use of the choir and in 1816 the *Choral Book* was published. This collection contained 110 psalm-tunes and hymns, principally from English and German sources. A few American tunes, among them Lewis Edson's popular *Lenox*, were included.

Lewis EDSON, Sr. (b. Bridgewater, Mass., 1748; d. near Woodstock, N.Y., 1820) was a blacksmith by trade, but early in life became an amateur musician. He first taught singing school and by 1780 had won considerable fame in Massachusetts, New York, and Connecticut as a singer. He was highly regarded by his contemporaries, although he compiled no tunebooks and composed comparatively little music. He did, however, write three of the most popular fuging tunes of his time. These were included in almost all later collections, and one of them, *Lenox*, may be found in modern hymnals. Edson's son, Lewis, Jr. (1771–1845), was a school teacher and singing master and published a collection called the *Social Harmonist* (New York, 1800).

Daniel Decatur EMMETT (b. Mt. Vernon, Ohio, 1815; d. there, 1904) was perhaps the most famous of the black-face performers. His entire life was spent in travel, first with a circus troupe at the age of eighteen and subsequently as a minstrel with several minstrel groups. In 1858 he led his own Emmett's Minstrels in a short-lived tour, but it was not until his association with Bryant's Minstrels in the same year that he began the composition of his famous minstrel songs and "walk-arounds."

Josiah FLAGG (b. Woburn, Mass., 1738; d. 1794) was a teacher, director of a military band, compiler-publisher of two collections, and an impresario. He organized concerts of "vocal and instrumental musick" and as early as 1771 performed music of Bach and Handel. His *Collection of the Best Psalm Tunes* (1764) included two anthems. In 1766 Flagg published a second collection, entitled *A Collection of All Tans'ur's and a number of other Anthems . . .*, which included upwards of twenty anthems, the first extensive collection of anthems published in America.

Stephen Collins FOSTER (b. Lawrenceville, near Pittsburgh, Penn., 1826; d. New York, 1864) showed an interest in music early in life but had little, if any, formal instruction. His first composition, *The Tioga Waltz*, was written at the age of fourteen while he was in school at Athens near Towanda. His first published song was composed when he was sixteen, and his interest in Negro melodies and black-face songs led to the composition in 1845 of the first of a large number of "Ethiopian" or minstrel songs. Foster lived with his parents in Allegheny from 1841 to 1846 and then moved to Cincinnati as a bookkeeper for his brother. He returned to Allegheny in 1848 and married Jane McDowell in 1850. In 1860 he went to New York with his wife and daughter and feverishly tried to make a living by selling his songs. Foster's limited education, inability to hold a position, and lack of business acumen, however, kept him in a perpetual state of debt. He finally became an alcoholic and died destitute in Bellevue Hospital. During his short lifetime of 38 years, Foster composed 188 songs (many to his own texts), twelve instrumental compositions, and a number of arrangements.

Jacob FRENCH (b. Stoughton, Mass., 1754; d. place and date unknown) was a singing master and an able and sensitive composer. He compiled three tunebooks (1789, 1793, 1802), but his own compositions were not often included in collections compiled by others.

William Henry FRY (b. Philadelphia, 1813, d. Santa Cruz, West Indies, 1864) was a composer, journalist, and champion of American music and opera in English. He went to Europe about 1845 as foreign editor of the New York *Tribune* and met several European composers, among them Berlioz. He returned to America in 1852 as music editor of the *Tribune*, which afforded him the opportunity to attack the indifference of artists and audiences to their own native composers. Fry's compositions include four symphonies—*Santa Claus*, *The Breaking Heart*, *Childe Harold*, and *A Day in the Country* (all performed by the eccentric Frenchman, Louis Antoine Jullien)—two operas, cantatas, and songs.

Patrick Sarsfield GILMORE (Louis Lambert) (b. Dublin, Ireland, 1829; d. St. Louis, Mo., 1892) came to the United States via Canada and became a bandmaster with the Union Army. He organized "Gilmore's Band" in 1859 and became famous for his mammoth "Peace Jubilees" requiring thousands of musicians. The "Worlds Peace Jubilee" held in Boston in 1882 required an orchestra of 2000 and a chorus of 20,000! His compositions include military music, songs, and arrangements for band.

Louis Moreau GOTTSCHALK (b. New Orleans, 1829; d. Tijuca, near Rio de Janeiro, 1869) was the son of an aristocratic Creole mother and an affluent English father. His parents recognized his extraordinary musical talent and he was sent to Paris to study in 1842. At the age of sixteen he was presented in a private concert in Salle Pleyel and in 1847 he made his professional début in Sedan, France, and in 1849 in Paris. Returning to the United States early in 1853, he gave his first New York recital at Niblo's Saloon and began a tour of the United States, invariably arousing his audiences, especially the ladies, to a high pitch of enthusiasm.

Gottschalk made a short Cuban tour in 1854, and from 1857 to 1862 he resided in Cuba, composing, wandering throughout the Caribbean islands giving concerts, and "enjoying the good life." On his return to the United States in 1862, he made his second début at Niblo's Garden and embarked on an even more hectic concert life than before.

From 1865 until his death, Gottschalk lived in South America, settling finally in Rio de Janeiro. Although stricken with yellow fever, he continued to give concerts and directed a gala festival concert on November 24, 1869, in which 650 musicians participated. He was invited to play during a concert by the Philharmonic Society the following day, and while playing his *Morte* he was taken ill and was unable to complete the composition. He died on December 18 and his body was interred in Rio de Janeiro. A year later his remains were returned to the United States and buried in Greenwood Cemetery, Brooklyn.

Gottschalk's works include 103 published pieces for piano, two operas, two symphonies, various works for orchestra, and a few songs.

Hans GRAM (b. Denmark, dates unknown) was educated in Stockholm and about 1789 settled in Boston, where he became organist of the Brattle Street Church. He collaborated with Oliver Holden and Samuel Holyoke in the publication of *The Massachusetts Compiler* (1795), a progressive and comprehensive work on psalmody which included a musical dictionary. Gram also composed a number of anthems and some songs that appeared in *The Massachusetts Magazine*.

Alice HAWTHORNE. See Septimus Winner.

Peter Albrecht van (von) HAGEN, Sr. (b. 1750, Holland; d. Boston, 1803), music teacher, organist, violinist, and composer, lived in Charleston, S.C., from 1774 to 1789. He then moved to New York with his musical family, which included his equally famous son, Peter Albrecht, Jr. (1781–1837). In 1796 he went to Boston, where he conducted the Haymarket Theatre Orchestra, became organist at the Stone Chapel (1800), taught music, and established a music shop and publishing house. His compositions include a number of patriotic songs and pieces and music for the theater.

Thomas HASTINGS (b. Washington, Conn., 1784; d. New York, 1872) was a self-taught composer of hymn-tunes and a compiler of successful tunebooks. His first collection appeared in 1816, and during the course of the years he brought out 50 volumes of music, some in collaboration with others. He is said to have composed some 1000 hymn-tunes and 600 hymn texts. Hastings was editor of the *Western Recorder* of Utica from 1823 to 1832. He then settled in New York, where he became associated with Lowell Mason and in 1836 founded the *Musical Magazine*. His *Dissertation on Musical Taste* appeared in 1822 and *The History of Forty Choirs* in 1854. In 1858 he received from the University of the City of New York one of the first honorary Doctor of Music degrees to be awarded in America.

Anthony Philip HEINRICH (b. Schönbüchel, Bohemia, 1781; d. New York, 1861) arrived in the United States about 1818; his continuous search for employment and recognition for his compositions took him to Philadelphia, Boston, Pittsburgh, Lexington (Kentucky), London, and New York. He found inspiration for his grandiose compositions in the Indians and in the history and natural beauty of his adopted country. In the Preface to his *Dawning of Music in Kentucky, or the Pleasures of Harmony in the Solitudes of Nature* he states that "no one would ever be more proud than himself, to be called an *American Musician*." After his many travels, Heinrich finally settled in New York and devoted himself to composing his American music and promoting his efforts by taking an active part in the musical life of the city. He composed an enormous number of orchestral compositions, cantatas, and songs, most of them with fanciful titles that were sometimes foreign or a mixture of languages. Heinrich met with many disappointments and some successes, but his lack of talent and training was all too apparent. He will be remembered, however, as one of the first to promote American nationalism.

James HEWITT (b. Dartmoor, England, 1770; d. Boston, 1827) left for the New World in 1792. A fine musician, he became a dominant personality in New York, where in addition to his activities as an organist, violinist, conductor, and composer, he operated a Musical Repository which he purchased from Benjamin Carr. In 1812 Hewitt moved to Boston, where he became associated with the Federal Street Theater, was organist of Trinity Church, and continued his other musical activities both in New York and Boston. Hewitt's compositions include sentimental ballads and other songs, keyboard pieces, among them *The Battle of Trenton*, and various orchestral works and theater music.

John Hill HEWITT (b. New York, 1801; d. Baltimore, 1890) was the eldest son of James Hewitt. Active as a theatrical manager, composer, and journalist, he achieved a modicum of fame when he bested Edgar Allen Poe in a literary contest with his poem *The Song of the Wind*. His compositions include about 300 songs, an oratorio, four cantatas, and four operas.

Oliver HOLDEN (b. Shirley, Mass., 1765; d. Charlestown, 1844) was a carpenter and Justice of the Peace in Charlestown. From about 1792 he began to teach music and operate a music store. He later became a preacher in the Puritan Church, and was elected to the Massachusetts House of Representatives. Many of his hymn-tunes were published in the *Union Harmony* (1793), and he contributed to some nine other collections between 1792 and 1807.

Samuel HOLYOKE (b. Boxford, Mass., 1762; d. Concord, N.H., 1820) was one of the few New England composers to whom music was more than an avocation. He graduated from Harvard in 1789 and after 1800 lived in Salem, teaching, conducting, and promoting concerts there and in other New England towns. Holyoke taught music at Phillips Andover Academy (1809–1810) and was active as a composer-compiler of tunebooks. His instruction book, *The Instrumental Assistant* (Exeter, New Hampshire, Vol. I, 1800; Vol. II, 1807), was one of the first to contain detailed instructions on the art of playing the violin, German flute, clarinet, hautboy, and bass-viol.

Francis HOPKINSON (b. Philadelphia, 1737; d. there, 1791), a member of a prominent Philadelphia family, graduated from the College of Philadelphia (now University of Pennsylvania). He was a poet, satirist, inventor, painter, and one of the signers of the Declaration of Independence. He became the first Secretary of the Navy and found time to receive musical instruction from James Bremner, to compose, and to perform at the harpsichord. His compositions include a number of songs, a few odes, and two of the earliest anthems by an American composer. He brought out a *Collection of Psalm Tunes* in 1763, and in 1767 he adapted psalms from the "New Version of Tate and Brady for the use of the Reformed Protestant Church in New York."

Jeremiah INGALLS (b. Andover, Mass., 1764; d. Hancock, Vt., 1828) was a tavern-keeper, farmer, cooper, singing-school teacher, composer, compiler, and choirmaster. He moved to Vermont in 1800, living successively in Newbury, Rochester, and Hancock. His compositions, some of them folk hymns, are found in his only collection, *The Christian Harmony* (Exeter, 1805), and other tunebooks, particularly in the South.

George K. JACKSON (b. Oxford, England, 1745; d. Boston, 1823) was awarded a Doctor of Music degree from Saint Andrews College in 1791 and left England for Virginia in 1796. He was in New York in 1804 as organist of St. George's Chapel, and in 1812 he settled in Boston and became the organist of the newly organized Handel and Haydn Choral Society. A prolific writer, he published hymn books, a treatise on music theory, and numerous compositions.

Stephen JENKS (b. New Canaan, Conn., 1772; d. Thompson, Ohio, 1856), composer and compiler of hymn-tunes, confined his activity principally to the state of Connecticut, although many of his tunes were well known in New England and the South. He compiled at least five tunebooks between 1800 and 1824.

Simeon JOCELIN (JOCELYN) (b. Branford, Conn., 1746; d. New Haven, 1823). Little is known about the life of this composer, but he compiled three collections (one with Amos Doolittle) between 1780 and 1793.

Jacob KIMBALL (b. Topsfield, Mass., 1761; d. there, 1826) graduated in law from Harvard in 1780 and was admitted to the bar in Stratford, N.H., but abandoned the profession for music. He studied with Hans Gram, organized singing classes, and taught in many New England towns. Kimball left two collections, *The Rural Harmony* (Boston, 1793), which contained over 70 of his tunes, and *The Essex Harmony* (Exeter, N.H., 1800).

E. J. KING (c. 1800–c. 1850) was associated with B. F. White in the publication of *The Sacred Harp* (Philadelphia, 1844).

Walter KITTREDGE (dates unknown) was called to the Northern Army in 1862, but rejected because of rheumatic fever. He is known today for his song *Tenting on the Old Camp Ground*, which met with great popular success.

Louis LAMBERT. See Patrick S. Gilmore

Andrew LAW (b. Milford, Conn., 1748; d. Cheshire, Conn., 1821) was educated at Rhode Island College (Brown University), where he received a master's degree. He became an ordained minister in 1787, but his interest in music led him to the profession of singing master, compiler, and composer. He invented a new system of notation (1802) which employed four (later seven) shape notes without the use of a staff and adopted—for the first time in American tunebooks—the idea of setting the melody in the treble instead of the tenor. Between 1767 and 1812 Law compiled a considerable number of tunebooks which went into several editions. His popular *Art of Singing* (1794) included in its three parts the *Musical Primer*, *Christian Harmony*, and *Musical Magazine*.

James LYON (b. Newark, N.J., 1735; d. Machias, Maine, 1794) was a student at New Jersey College

(Nassau Hall) which moved to Princeton in 1756 and became known as Princeton University. He graduated in 1759 with a B.A. degree and in 1762, while living in Philadelphia, he received his M.A. degree. He was ordained a Presbyterian minister in 1764 and was sent to Nova Scotia and in 1771 to Machias, Maine, where he remained until his death. His first composition was an ode, which was performed in 1759 at the time of his graduation from Princeton. In 1761 an anthem of his and an ode by Francis Hopkinson were performed at a commencement program given by the College of Pennsylvania in Philadelphia. Ten of Lyon's compositions have been preserved, six of them in *Urania* (Philadelphia, 1761)—his only collection.

Lowell MASON (b. Medfield, Mass., 1792; d. Orange, N.J., 1872) was largely a self-taught musician, although he received some instruction from Oliver Shaw and others. In 1812 he moved to Savannah, Georgia, where he worked in a bank and was organist and choirmaster at the First Presbyterian Church. While there he studied harmony and composition and compiled his first collection, published in Boston in 1822. In 1827 Mason moved to Boston, where he was elected president of the Handel and Haydn Society and became organist of Lyman Beecher's Church. He established the Boston Academy of Music in 1832 and in 1838 succeeded in introducing music in the public schools. His teachers' institutes, normal institutes, and musical conventions spread his work throughout the country. Mason made two trips to Europe; in 1837 to study the Pestalozzian system of teaching and from 1851 to 1853 to lecture. He received an honorary Doctor of Music degree from New York University in 1855, the second to be awarded in this country. Mason composed a large number of hymns and published about eighteen collections of sacred music, some in collaboration with his colleagues, which brought him enormous profits. He also compiled fifteen books for children and a number of collections of secular part-songs and glees.

William MASON (b. Boston, 1829; d. New York, 1908) was the youngest son of Lowell Mason. After piano instruction with Henry Schmidt in Boston, Mason went to Europe in 1849. He studied in Leipzig with Moscheles, Hauptmann, and Richter; in Prague with Dreyschock and with Liszt in Weimar. Mason played a number of recitals in Europe—not always with unqualified success—before returning to New York in 1854. He took up the career of a piano virtuoso, but disliked the taste of a public that demanded such improvisations as the playing of *Old Hundredth* and *Yankee Doodle* at the same time. With Theodore Thomas he founded in 1855 the "Soirées of Chamber-music" for the performance of Classical music, a series that continued until 1868. He devoted himself more and more to teaching and composing and achieved an enviable reputation as a piano pedagogue. In addition to his well-known textbooks on piano playing, including the important *Touch and Technic* (1891), Mason composed about 40 piano pieces and a *Serenata* for cello and piano.

David Moritz MICHAEL (b. Kienhausen [Erfurt], Germany, 1751; d. Neuwied, Germany, 1827) arrived in America in 1795. He became a dominant figure in Moravian music, first in Nazareth and then in Bethlehem. He was much interested in contemporary European music and gave the first American performance of Haydn's *The Creation* at Bethlehem in 1811. Michael composed anthems, songs, and sixteen pieces for wind instruments.

John MILTON, Sr. (b. near Oxford c. 1563; d. London, 1647), father of the poet, was a chorister at Christ Church, Oxford (c. 1573–77), and in 1585 went to London, where he was admitted to the Scriveners' Company. His compositions include a madrigal, anthems, motets, three psalm-settings in Ravenscroft's Psalter, and two *Fantazias* for viols.

John Christopher MOLLER (probably born in Germany; d. New York, 1803) arrived in New York from London in 1790 and made his first appearance as a harpsichordist. Shortly thereafter he was appointed organist at Zion Church in Philadelphia and took an active part in the City Concerts. Besides his activities as a keyboard performer, composer, and teacher, he founded with Capron the first publishing firm in Philadelphia which he also used as a music school. He was in New York in 1796; there he succeeded Hewitt as manager of the New York City Concerts with the van Hagens. Moller published a considerable number of compositions including string quartets, keyboard sonatas, and instruction books.

Justin MORGAN (b. West Springfield, Mass., 1747; d. Randolph, Vt., 1798) is perhaps better known as a horse breeder than as a hymn-tune writer. He did not publish any collections, and his many tunes are found in the compilations of others.

Victor PELISSIER (dates unknown), a horn virtuoso and composer, was a post-Revolutionary emigrant from France. He first worked in Philadelphia and in 1793 he went to New York, where he was principal horn-player and composer and arranger for the Old American Company. He wrote a number of ballad operas and incidental music for plays and pantomimes.

Johann Friedrich (John Frederik) PETER (b. Heerendijk, Holland, 1746, of German parents; d. Bethlehem, 1813) came to Pennsylvania in 1770, served in various capacities in Nazareth, Bethlehem, and Lititz, and became director of the Collegium Musicum in Salem, N.C., where he lived from 1780 to 1790. He spent a few years in Graceham, Maryland, and Hope, New Jersey, after which he returned to Bethlehem. Peter composed some 116 anthems and six string quintets and copied and performed a considerable amount of music by Stamitz, C. P. E. Bach, and others.

Philip PHILE (b. c. 1734; d. Philadelphia, 1793) was a German violinist and teacher who came to Philadelphia early in the 1780s. He served in the Pennsylvania regiment during the Revolutionary War and participated in musical affairs as a violinist and conductor in New York and Philadelphia.

Daniel READ (b. Attleboro, Mass., 1757; d. New Haven, Conn., 1836) spent the greater part of his life in New Haven as a comb-maker, owner of a general store, and singing master. He was one of the most capable composers of the late 18th century, and his tunebooks were widely known. Read's two principal collections were *The American Singing Book* (New Haven, 1785 to 1796) with its *Supplement* (1787) and *The Columbian Harmonist* (New Haven, 1793 to 1810).

Alexander REINAGLE (b. Portsmouth, England, 1756; d. Baltimore, 1809) was born of Austrian parents. He was a pupil of Raynor Taylor in London and counted among his close friends C. P. E. Bach, whose musical style he greatly admired. Coming to America in 1786, he settled in Philadelphia and established himself as a pianist, composer, conductor, theatrical manager, and teacher. He was one of the founders and musical director for fifteen years of a company organized for the production of ballad operas. Reinagle wrote instrumental works for keyboard, strings, pantomimes, and stage plays, and a collection of songs.

Thomas Dartmouth ("Daddy") RICE (b. New York, 1808; d. there, 1860), singer and comedian, popularized black-face characterizations with his routine, which he called "Jump Jim Crow."

Henry RUSSELL (b. Sheerness, England, 1812; d. London, 1900) was an organist, singer, and composer of sentimental ballads. He spent some time in Italy and Paris, where he met many of the famous musicians of the time. He came to America in 1833 and was organist of the First Presbyterian Church in Rochester, N.Y., until 1841, when he returned to England. During this time he composed hundreds of ballads and traveled extensively throughout the United States, singing his songs to his own accompaniments and meeting with extraordinary success.

William SELBY (b. England, 1738; d. Boston, 1798) was an organist, harpsichordist, composer, teacher, and concert manager. He came to Boston about 1771 and, except for a short time in Newport, R.I., remained there the rest of his life. Shortly after his arrival he was appointed organist at King's Chapel, and during the Revolution he made his living as a liquor dealer and grocer. After the war he resumed his career and played an important part in the rapid development of music in Boston. Selby's compositions include songs, anthems, and instrumental pieces.

Oliver SHAW (b. Middleboro, Mass., 1779; d. Providence, R.I., 1848) was for a time a dealer in pianofortes, music, and fish, advertising the piscatorial product in his *Melodia Sacra* (Providence, 1819) as "one Barrel extra No. 1 Mackeral." A good part of his musical education was received from Gottlieb Graupner, who arrived in Boston in 1796. In 1807 he settled in Providence as a singing teacher and organist of the First Congregational Church. Deprived of his sight at twenty-one, he nevertheless acquired an enviable reputation as a composer and teacher, numbering among his many pupils Lowell Mason. Shaw composed mostly sacred music—hymns, psalm-tunes, songs—and compiled three collections of sacred music. His secular compositions include instrumental ensembles published in *For the Gentlemen* (Dedham, 1807) and a few songs.

William STEFFE (dates unknown) of Charleston, S. C., was a composer of popular Sunday School songs. The tune of the famous *Battle Hymn of the Republic* is attributed to him.

Timothy SWAN (b. Worcester, Mass., 1758; d. Northfield, Mass., 1842) was a carpenter and virtually a self-taught composer. His musical education consisted of a few weeks in a singing school, and while serving in the Continental Army he learned to play the fife. In 1773 he was living in Suffield, Conn., and in 1807 he moved to Northfield, Mass. Between 1785 and 1803 Swan compiled two and possibly three collections, which included a number of his own hymn-tunes and a few secular songs.

William TANS'UR (Tanzer) (b. Dunchurch, Warwickshire, 1706; d. St. Neot's, Huntingdonshire, 1783) was a bookbinder, theoretician, teacher of psalmody, and a composer-compiler of psalm-tunes and anthems. His publications were numerous and went into many editions.

Raynor TAYLOR (b. England, 1747; d. Philadelphia, 1825) was trained as a chorister of the King's Royal Chapel and in 1765 became organist of a church in Chelmsford. In the same year he was appointed music director of Sadler's Wells Theatre in London. He came to the United States in 1792 and was well-equipped to serve in the roles of conductor, impresario, organist, singer, and composer. He first lived in Baltimore, then Annapolis, and from 1793 in Philadelphia, where he played a dual role as organist of St. Peter's Church and impresario-entertainer of comic skits known as "Olios." His works are mostly secular and include a ballad opera, cantatas, songs, and instrumental pieces.

William TUCKEY (b. Somersetshire, England, 1708; d. Philadelphia, 1781) played an important part in the musical life of New York from his arrival there in 1753. He organized the choir at Trinity Church, taught music, and was active as a concert artist. In 1770 he presented the Overture and sixteen numbers from Handel's *Messiah* for the first time in America. Tuckey's compositions, widely known in his lifetime, include anthems, odes, and psalm-tunes. He published none of his own music, however, but his works are found in the compilations of others.

John TUFTS (b. Medford, Mass., 1689; d. Amesbury, Mass., 1750) graduated from Harvard College in 1708. He was a Congregational minister in Newbury, Mass., from 1714 until his retirement in 1738 to Amesbury, where he became a shopkeeper. He was a pioneer in music instruction and tunebooks.

William WALKER (b. Cross Keys, S.C., 1809; d. Spartansburg, S.C., 1875) was born of humble parents and received very little education. His ambition to "perfect the vocal modes of praise" resulted in the compilation of *The Southern Harmony* (1835). This enormously popular collection contained 209 tunes, of which Walker claimed the authorship of 25. Later editions included fifteen more of his folk hymns.

Thomas WALTER (b. Roxbury, Mass., 1696; d. there, 1725) received his M.A. degree from Harvard College in 1713, and in 1718 he became an ordained minister. Like Tufts, he recognized the need for music instruction books, and in 1721, just four years before his death at the age of twenty-nine, he published his *Grounds and Rules of Musick Explained*.

George James WEBB (b. near Salisbury, England, 1803; d. Orange, N.J., 1887) studied piano, violin, and organ in his youth and in 1830 came to Boston. He was appointed organist of the Old South Church and helped Lowell Mason organize the Boston Academy of Music. He became famous as a choral and orchestral conductor and in 1840 was made president of the Handel and Haydn Society. In 1870 he followed Mason to New York, where he taught voice and conducted normal courses for teachers. Webb's compositions include sacred songs, glees, cantatas, and hymn-tunes. He compiled a number of collections of church music, some with Mason, and edited two periodicals, *The Musical Library* (1835–1836) and *The Musical Cabinet* (1837–1840).

Benjamin Franklin WHITE (b. Spartansburg, S.C., 1800; d. Atlanta, Ga., 1879) was a newspaper editor and a self-taught musician. He became a singing teacher, composer, arranger, and published *The Sacred Harp* (1844) with E. J. King.

Aaron WILLIAMS (b. London, 1731; d. there, 1776) was a music teacher, engraver, publisher, and a clerk at the Scottish Church in London Wall. He composed anthems and hymn-tunes and published four collections between 1763 and 1780 for use in Nonconformist churches.

Septimus WINNER (Alice Hawthorne) (b. Philadelphia, 1827; d. there, 1902) began to earn his living as a music teacher, giving lessons in violin, banjo, guitar, and other instruments. In 1847 he opened a publishing house and music store in Philadelphia. He is said to have composed over 200 volumes of music, including instruction books for 23 different instruments, arrangements for violin and pianoforte, and over 100 songs. His most famous song, *Listen to the Mocking Bird*, sold over 20 million copies in 50 years.

Abraham WOOD (b. Northboro, Mass., 1752; d. there, 1804) was a fuller, or dresser of cloth, a singer, and a self-taught composer. During the Revolutionary War he served as a drummer. He published his *Divine Songs* in 1789, and was co-author of the *Columbian Harmony* (1793) with Joseph Stone. Twenty-six of his tunes appeared in the latter collection and a number were published in other tunebooks.

Isaac Baker WOODBURY (b. Beverley, Mass., 1819; d. Columbia, S.C., 1858) was originally apprenticed to a blacksmith. He early became interested in music, however, and in 1838 went to Europe, where he studied in Paris and London. After a year he returned to America and settled in Boston as a music teacher and traveled with the Bay State Glee Club. He became known as a conductor in Vermont and later went to New York as a choirmaster at the Rutgers Street Church and became editor of *The Musical Review*. Woodbury wrote hymn-tunes, sacred and secular songs, and glees. He published a number of tunebooks that were extremely popular and a *Self-instructor in Musical Composition and Thorough-Bass*.

Henry Clay WORK (b. Middletown, Conn., 1832; d. Hartford, 1884) was a printer, an abolitionist, and a temperance advocate, but is remembered today as a self-taught composer of popular songs. Work is best known for his Civil War songs, but he was also a successful composer of minstrel and temperance songs.

General Index

Classified Index

S-Soprano; A-Alto; T-Tenor; B-Bass

I. VOCAL (unaccompanied)

Index of First Lines

This anthology presents 139 musical compositions spanning nearly 250 years. They attest to a surprising amount of activity in all media, conceived within a periphery extending from Massachusetts to Georgia, Louisiana, and Ohio. Drawing from an extensive body of metrical psalms, psalm-settings, sacred and secular choral works, solo songs, keyboard pieces, opera, and music for small instrumental groups, the editors present a panorama of musical landmarks that have played an important part in the spiritual, social, and artistic life of our country.

The music, presented in approximately chronological order, has been selected on the basis of its artistic significance and musico-historical importance in American history. With the exception of the chapter devoted to the music of the Moravians, the music has been taken from the first or earliest available